BUSINESS ECONOMICS IN A RAPIDLY-CHA

ECONOMIC CONTRIBUTIONS OF NATIONAL PARK VISITATIONS

ANALYSES OF SPENDING EFFECTS

BUSINESS ECONOMICS IN A RAPIDLY-CHANGING WORLD

Additional books in this series can be found on Nova's website under the Series tab.

Additional e-books in this series can be found on Nova's website under the e-book tab.

BUSINESS ECONOMICS IN A RAPIDLY-CHANGING WORLD

ECONOMIC CONTRIBUTIONS OF NATIONAL PARK VISITATIONS

ANALYSES OF SPENDING EFFECTS

JENELL MEEHAN
EDITOR

New York

For permission to use material from this book please contact us:
Telephone 631-231-7269; Fax 631-231-8175
Web Site: http://www.novapublishers.com

Additional color graphics may be available in the e-book version of this book.

Library of Congress Cataloging-in-Publication Data

ISBN: 978-1-60876-005-3

Published by Nova Science Publishers, Inc. † New York

CONTENTS

PREFACE

The National Park Service (NPS) manages the nation's most iconic destinations that attract millions of visitors from across the nation and around the world. Trip-related spending by NPS visitors generates and supports a considerable amount of economic activity within park gateway communities. This book provides an economic effects analysis which measures how NPS visitor spending cycles through local economies, generating business sales and supporting jobs and income.

Chapter 1 - The National Park Service (NPS) manages the nation's most iconic destinations that attract millions of visitors from across the nation and around the world. Trip-related spending by NPS visitors generates and supports a considerable amount of economic activity within park gateway communities. This economic effects analysis measures how NPS visitor spending cycles through local economies, generating business sales and supporting jobs and income.

In 2012, the National Park System received over 282 million recreation visits. NPS visitors spent $14.7 billion in local gateway regions (defined as communities within 60 miles of a park). The contribution of this spending to the national economy was 243 thousand jobs, $9.3 billion in labor income, $15.8 billion in value added, and $26.8 billion in output. The lodging sector saw the highest direct contributions with more than 40 thousand jobs and $4.5 billion in output directly contributed to local gateway economies nationally. The sector with the next greatest direct contributions was restaurants and bars, with 51 thousand jobs and $3 billion in output directly contributed to local gateway economies nationally.

This 2012 analysis marks a major revision to the NPS visitor spending effects analyses, with the development of a new visitor spending effects model

(VSE model) that replaces the former Money Generation Model (MGM2). Many of the hallmarks and processes of the MGM2 model are preserved in the new VSE model, but the new model makes significant strides in improving the accuracy and transparency of the analysis. Because of this change from the MGM2 model to the VSE model, estimates from this year's analysis are not directly comparable to previous analyses.

Chapter 2 - The National Park System received 278.9 million recreation visits in 2011. Park visitors spent $12.95 billion in local gateway regions (within roughly 60 miles of the park). Visitors staying overnight outside the park (in motels, hotels, cabins, and bed and breakfasts) accounted for 54.9% of the total spending. About half (48%) of the spending was for lodging and meals, 21.4% for gas and local transportation, 9.7% for recreation and entertainment, 8.1% for groceries, and 12.7% for other retail purchases.

The contribution of this park visitor spending to the national economy amounted to 251,600 jobs, $9.34 billion in labor income, and $16.50 billion in value added[1]. The direct effects of visitor spending are measured at the local level in gateway regions around national parks. Local economic impacts were estimated after excluding spending by park visitors from the local area (9.8% of the total spending). Combining local impacts across all parks yielded a total local impact (including direct and secondary effects) of 162,400 jobs, $4.58 billion in labor income, and $8.15 billion value added. The four local economic sectors most directly affected by non-local visitor spending are lodging, restaurants, retail trade, and recreation and entertainment. Their spending supported 45,200 jobs in restaurants and bars, 34,100 jobs in lodging sectors, 15,500 jobs in retail and wholesale trade, and 20,000 jobs in recreation and entertainment.

In this 2011 study, payroll impacts were not included due to the conversion to a new accounting system for the National Park Service, which prevented obtaining the required inputs for such analysis in time for publication.

Chapter 3 - The National Park System received 281 million recreation visits in 2010. Park visitors spent $12.13 billion in local gateway regions (within roughly 60 miles of the park). Visitors staying outside the park in motels, hotels, cabins and bed and breakfasts accounted for 56% of the total spending. Half of the spending was for lodging and meals, 19% for gas and local transportation, 10% for amusements, 8% for groceries, and 13% for other retail purchases.

The contribution of this spending to the national economy is 258,400 jobs, $9.8 billion in labor income, and $16.6 billion in value added[1]. The direct effects of visitor spending are at the local level in gateway regions around national parks. Local economic impacts were estimated after excluding spending by visitors from the local area (9.8% of the total). Combining local impacts across all parks yields a total local impact including direct and secondary effects of 156,280 jobs, $4.68 billion in labor income, and $7.65 billion value added. The four local economic sectors most directly affected by non-local visitor spending are lodging, restaurants, retail trade, and amusements. Visitor spending supports 43,160 jobs in restaurants and bars, 32,000 jobs in lodging sectors, 23,000 jobs in retail and wholesale trade, and 18,560 jobs in amusements.

Parks also impact the local and national economies through the NPS payroll. In Fiscal Year 2010 the National Park Service employed 26,031 people with a total payroll of $1,709 million in wages, salaries, and payroll benefits. Including the induced effects of the spending of NPS wages and salaries in the local region, the total local economic impacts of park payrolls are $1.95 billion in labor income, $2.16 billion in value added, and 32,407 jobs (including NPS jobs). The impacts of the park payroll on the national economy are $2.41 billion in labor income, $2.96 billion in value added, and 41,700 jobs Combining the impacts of non-local visitor spending and NPS payroll-related spending yields a total impact of 300,000 jobs nationally of which 189,000 are in the local regions around national parks.

In: Economic Contributions of National Park ... ISBN: 978-1-60876-005-3
Editor: Jenell Meehan

Chapter 1

2012 National Park Visitor Spending Effects: Economic Contributions to Local Communities, States, and the Nation*

Catherine Cullinane Thomas, Christopher Huber and Lynne Koontz

Executive Summary

The National Park Service (NPS) manages the nation's most iconic destinations that attract millions of visitors from across the nation and around the world. Trip-related spending by NPS visitors generates and supports a considerable amount of economic activity within park gateway communities. This economic effects analysis measures how NPS visitor spending cycles through local economies, generating business sales and supporting jobs and income.

In 2012, the National Park System received over 282 million recreation visits. NPS visitors spent $14.7 billion in local gateway regions (defined as communities within 60 miles of a park). The contribution of this spending to the national economy was 243 thousand jobs, $9.3 billion in labor income,

---

* This is an edited, reformatted and augmented version of Natural Resource Report NPS/NRSS/EQD/NRR—2014/765, issued by the National Park Service, February 2014.

$15.8 billion in value added, and $26.8 billion in output. The lodging sector saw the highest direct contributions with more than 40 thousand jobs and $4.5 billion in output directly contributed to local gateway economies nationally. The sector with the next greatest direct contributions was restaurants and bars, with 51 thousand jobs and $3 billion in output directly contributed to local gateway economies nationally.

This 2012 analysis marks a major revision to the NPS visitor spending effects analyses, with the development of a new visitor spending effects model (VSE model) that replaces the former Money Generation Model (MGM2). Many of the hallmarks and processes of the MGM2 model are preserved in the new VSE model, but the new model makes significant strides in improving the accuracy and transparency of the analysis. Because of this change from the MGM2 model to the VSE model, estimates from this year's analysis are not directly comparable to previous analyses.

ACKNOWLEDGMENTS

The authors would like to acknowledge Bruce Peacock, Rudyard Bartz, Susan Winter, Doug Smith, Kawa Ng, Philip Cook, Butch Street, Bret Meldrum, Eric White, and Elizabeth Donovan for your fabulous help in developing the new VSE model. We could not have done it without you.

INTRODUCTION

The National Park System covers more than 84 million acres and is comprised of 401 sites across the nation. These lands managed by the National Park Service (NPS) serve as recreational destinations for visitors from across the nation and around the world. On vacations or on day trips, NPS visitors spend time and money in the gateway communities surrounding NPS sites. Spending by NPS visitors generates and supports a considerable amount of economic activity within park gateway communities. This economic effects analysis measures how spending by NPS visitors cycles through local gateway economies, generating business sales and supporting jobs and income.

The NPS has been measuring and reporting visitor spending and economic effects for the past 24 years; and for the past 14 years, these estimates have been made using the Money Generation Model (MGM2). For the 2012 analysis, the NPS in collaboration with the U.S. Geological Survey (USGS) has developed a new model (the visitor spending effects model, or VSE model) to estimate visitor spending and economic effects. This report starts by describing the new VSE model and how it differs from the MGM2 model. Next, an overview of economic effects analyses is presented, followed by details about the data and methods used for this analysis. The report concludes by presenting estimates of NPS visitor spending in 2012 and resulting economic effects at the local, state, regional, and national levels. Park-level spending and economic effects estimates are included in the appendix.

New in 2012

This 2012 analysis marks a major revision to the NPS visitor spending effects analyses, with the development of a new visitor spending effects model (VSE model). The VSE model replaces the MGM2 model. Many of the hallmarks and processes of the MGM2 model are preserved in the new VSE model, but the new model makes significant strides in improving the accuracy and transparency of the analysis. It is important to note that, because of this change from the MGM2 model to the VSE model, estimates from this year's analysis are not directly comparable to previous analyses. The following bullets highlight the major differences between the MGM2 model and the new VSE model.

- Both the MGM2 and the VSE models rely on economic multipliers derived from the IMPLAN input-output modeling system. The VSE model improves upon the MGM2 model by using unique IMPLAN multipliers for each park. Park-level multipliers are based on county-level data for the local gateway economies surrounding each park.
- This year's analysis uses the most current 2012 IMPLAN data (IMPLAN Group LLC).
- Local gateway regions are redefined. As with the MGM2 model, local gateway regions are defined as all counties within a 60-mile radius surrounding park boundaries. The actual local gateway regions for the MGM2 model were modified from this rule set and tended to be smaller. For the VSE model, GIS data were used to determine the local gateway region for each park unit by spatially identifying all counties partially or completely contained within a 60-mile radius around each park boundary. This method creates a uniform definition

of local gateway regions. The new larger gateway regions capture a greater portion of secondary spending, and thus result in slightly larger local secondary effects.

- Visitor spending and trip characteristic data has changed for the VSE model from what were previously used in the MGM2 model. Although data used in both the VSE model and the MGM2 were derived from Visitor Services Project (VSP) surveys, the estimated generic visitor spending patterns and trip characteristic information differ. Generic profiles for the VSE model were developed using the VSP data categorized by four park types: parks that have both camping and lodging available within the park, parks that have only camping available within the park, parks with no overnight stays, and parks with high day use.

Overview of Economic Effects Analyses

Visitors to NPS lands spend money in local gateway regions, and these expenditures generate and support economic activity within these local economies. Economies are complex webs of interacting consumers and producers in which goods produced by one sector of an economy become inputs to another, and the goods produced by that sector can become inputs to yet other sectors. Thus, a change in the final demand for a good or service can generate a ripple effect throughout an economy as businesses purchase inputs from one another. For example, when visitors come to an area to visit a park or historic site these visitors spend money to purchase various goods and services. The sales, income and employment resulting from these direct purchases from local businesses represent the *direct* effects of visitor spending within the economy. In order to provide supplies to local businesses for the production of their goods and services, input suppliers must purchase inputs from other industries, thus creating additional *indirect* effects of visitor spending within the economy. Additionally, employees of directly affected businesses and input suppliers use their income to purchase goods and services in the local economy, generating further *induced* effects of visitor spending. The sums of the indirect and induced effects give the *secondary* effects of visitor spending; and the sums of the direct and secondary effects give the total economic effect of visitor spending in the local economy. Economic input-output models capture these complex interactions between producers and consumers in an economy and describe the secondary effects of visitor spending through regional economic multipliers.

Types of Economic Effects Measured

The economic effects of visitor spending to local economies are estimated by multiplying visitor spending by regional economic multipliers. Two regional economic metrics, economic contributions and economic impacts, are described in this report:

- *Economic contributions* describe the gross change in economic activity associated with National Park visitor spending within a regional economy. Economic contribution can be interpreted as the relative magnitude and importance to regional economies of the economic activity generated through National Park visitor spending. Economic contributions are estimated by multiplying *total visitor spending* by regional economic multipliers. Total visitor spending includes spending by both visitors that live within the local gateway regions (local visitors) and visitors that travel to the parks from outside of the local gateway regions (non-local visitors). Note: economic contribution was referred to as "economic significance" in previous MGM reports.
- *Economic impacts* describe the net changes to the economic base of a regional economy that can be attributed to the inflow of new money to the economy from non-local visitors. Economic impact estimates only include spending by non-local visitors. Spending by local visitors is excluded because if local visitors choose not to visit the park, they will still likely spend a similar amount of money within the local economy participating in other local recreation activities. Economic impacts can be interpreted as the economic activity that would likely be lost from the local economy if the National Park were not there.

For both of these metrics, four types of regional economic effects are described:

- **Output** represents the value of industry production. Output is the sum of all intermediate sales (business to business) and final demand (sales to consumers and exports). Note: output was referred to as "Sales" in previous MGM reports.

- **Employment** represents the change in the number of jobs generated in a region resulting from a change in regional output. Employment is measured as annualized full and part time jobs.
- **Labor income** includes employee wages and salaries, including the income of sole proprietors and payroll benefits.
- **Value added** measures contribution to Gross Domestic Product (GDP). Value added is equal to the difference between the amount an industry sells a product for and the production cost of the product.

Economic Regions

In order to assess the economic effects of NPS visitor spending, appropriate local regions needed to be defined around each park unit. For the purposes of this analysis, the local gateway region for each park unit is defined as all counties contained within or intersecting a 60-mile radius around each park boundary[1].

GIS data were used to determine the local gateway region for each park unit by spatially identifying all counties partially or completely contained within a 60-mile radius around each park boundary[2]. Only spending that took place within these regional areas is included as stimulating changes in economic activity.

Data Sources and Methods

Three key pieces of information are required to estimate the economic effects of NPS visitor spending: the number of visitors who visit each park, visitor spending patterns in local gateway regions, and regional economic multipliers that describe the economic effects of visitor spending in local economies.

Visitation source data are derived from a variety of efforts by the NPS Social Science Program. The data sources and methods used to estimate these inputs and the resultant economic effects are described below.

Recreation Visitation Estimates

The NPS Visitor Use Statistics Office (https://irma.nps.gov/Stats/) provides detailed park-level visitation data for 369 National Park units. The annual NPS recreation visitation estimates published in the 2012 Statistical Abstract (Street, 2013) are used for this analysis. The abstract reports the number of overnight camping and lodging stays within the parks. For each park, visitation is measured as *visits*[3]. Visitation estimates must be adjusted based on trip characteristic data in order to develop an estimate of visitation that is useful for estimating total visitor spending. Adjustments to visitation estimates are described in the visitor spending estimates section below.

Visitor Spending Estimates

The NPS has conducted Visitor Services Project (VSP) surveys since 1988. These surveys measure visitor characteristics and satisfaction at select parks, and a subset of the VSP surveys include questions on visitor spending. Fifty-six VSP surveys conducted between 2003 and 2012 have the requisite data necessary to estimate park-level visitor spending profiles for this analysis. Spending data for the 56 surveyed parks were adjusted to 2012 dollars, and were used to represent spending patterns at the surveyed parks. Non-surveyed parks were classified into four park types: parks that have both camping and lodging available within the park, parks that have only camping available within the park, parks with no overnight stays, and parks with high day use (including National Recreation Areas, National Seashores and National Lakeshores). Generic spending profiles for each of these park types were developed using data from the 56 surveyed parks. A number of parks are not well represented by the four park types constructed using the VSP survey data. For these parks, profiles were constructed using the best available data. These units include parks in Alaska, parks in the Washington D.C. area, parkways, and parks in highly urban areas. Profiles were also constructed for a number of unique parks.

Visitor spending data from the VSP surveys are reported as spending per party per night for overnight trips, and spending per party per day for day trips. A party is defined as a group that is traveling together and sharing expenses (e.g. a family). Party days/nights are defined as the number of days (for day trips) and the number of nights (for overnight trips) that parties spend visiting a park. To estimate total party days/nights, park visit data from the NPS

Statistical Abstract are combined with trip characteristic information derived from the VSP surveys. Trip characteristic data includes average party sizes, re-entry rates, and lengths of stay. Visitation data are converted to total party days/nights using the following conversion:

$$Total\ party\ days/nights = \frac{Visits}{Party\ Size} * \frac{1}{ReEntry\ Rate} * Length\ of\ Stay$$

The VSP data is also used to segment visitors by type of trip. NPS recreation visitors are split into the following seven distinct **visitor segments** in order to help explain differences in spending across user groups:

- *Local day trip*: local visitors who visit the park for a single day and leave the area or return home,
- *Non-local day trip*: non-local visitors who visit the park for a single day and leave the area or return home,
- *NPS Lodge*: non-local visitors who stay at a lodge or motel within the park,
- *NPS Campground*: non-local visitors who stay at campgrounds or at back country camping sites within the park,
- *Motel Outside Park*: non-local visitors who stay at motels, hotels, or bed and breakfasts located outside of the park,
- *Camp Outside Park*: non-local visitors who camp outside of the park, and
- *Other*: non-local visitors who stay overnight in the local region but do not have any lodging expenses. This segment includes visitors staying in private homes, with friends or relatives, or in other unpaid lodging.

Spending is further broken into the following eight **spending categories** derived from the VSP survey data:

- Hotels, motels and bed and breakfasts,
- Camping fees,
- Restaurants and bars,
- Groceries and takeout food,
- Gas and oil,
- Local transportation,
- Admission and fees, and
- Souvenirs and other expenses.

Regional Economic Multipliers

The multipliers used in this analysis are derived from the IMPLAN software and data system (IMPLAN Group LLC). IMPLAN is a widely used input-output modeling system. The underlying data drawn upon by the IMPLAN system are collected by the IMPLAN Group LLC from multiple Federal and state sources including the Bureau of Economic Analysis, Bureau of Labor Statistics, and the U.S. Census Bureau. This analysis uses IMPLAN version 3.0 software with 2012 county, state, and national-level data. Economic effects are reported on an annual basis in 2012 dollars ($2012). Where necessary, dollar values have been adjusted to $2012 using historic Bureau of Economic Analysis (BEA) output and value-added deflators.

This analysis reports economic impacts and contributions at the local-level, and economic contributions at the state, NPS region, and national levels. Local economic impacts and contributions use county-level IMPLAN models comprised of all counties contained within the local gateway regions; state-level contributions use state-level IMPLAN models; regional-level contributions use regional IMPLAN models; and the national-level contributions use a national IMPLAN model. The size of the region included in an IMPLAN model influences the magnitude of the economic multiplier effects. As the economic region expands, the amount of secondary spending that stays within that region increases, which results in larger economic multipliers. Thus, contributions at the national level are larger than those at the regional, state, and local levels.

RESULTS

Recreation Visits

A total of 282.8 million NPS recreation visits are reported in the 2012 NPS Statistical Abstract (Street, 2013). This is up 3.9 million visits over 2011 visitation. Total party days/nights are estimated for each park unit and for each visitor segment based on visitor segments splits (as described in the *visitor spending estimates* section). In 2012, visitor groups accounted for 114.4 million party days/nights. Figure 1 provides total party days/nights by visitor segment.

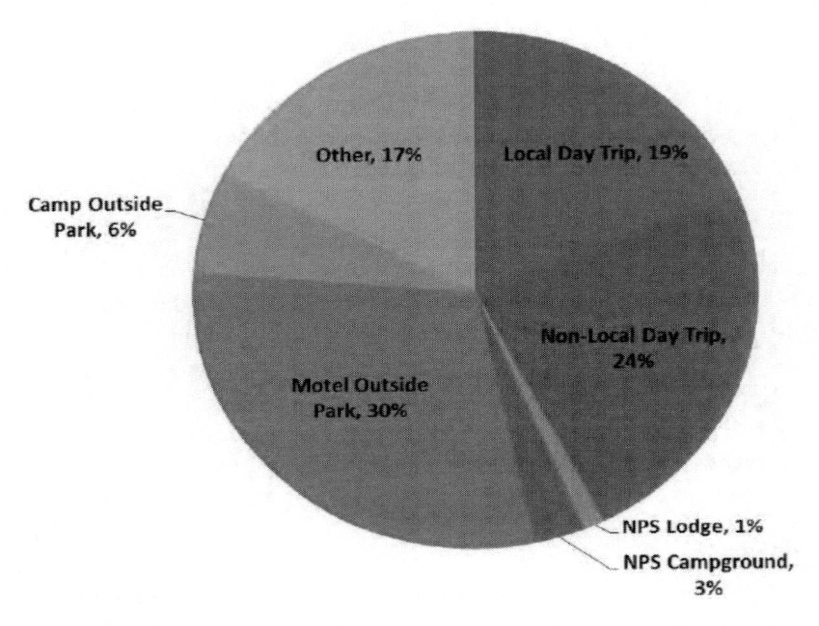

Figure 1. Distribution of total party days/nights by visitor segment. Total party days/nights measures the number of days (for day trips) and nights (for overnight trips) that visitor groups spend in gateway communities while visiting NPS lands.

Visitor Spending

In 2012, park visitors spent an estimated $14.7 billion in local gateway regions while visiting NPS lands. Visitor spending was estimated for each park unit and for each visitor segment based on park and segment specific expenditure profiles (as described in the *visitor spending estimates* section). Total visitor spending is equal to total party days/nights multiplied by spending per party per day/night. Table 1 gives total spending estimates and average spending per party per day/night by visitor segment. Figure 2 presents the distribution of visitor spending by spending category. Lodging expenses account for the largest share of visitor spending. In 2012, park visitors spent $4.5 billion on lodging in hotels, motels and bed and breakfasts, and an additional $358.9 million on camping fees. Food expenses account for the next largest share of expenditures. In 2012, park visitors spent over $2.9 billion dining at restaurants and bars and an additional $1.1 billion purchasing food at grocery and convenience stores.

Table 1. NPS visitor spending estimates for 2012

Visitor Segment	Total Spending ($ Millions)	Percent of Total Spending	Average spending per party per day/night ($)
Local Day Trip	$855.2	6%	$39.74
Non-Local Day Trip	$2,371.1	16%	$87.16
NPS Lodge	$490.5	3%	$375.73
NPS Camp Ground	$443.8	3%	$128.65
Motel Outside Park	$8,900.3	60%	$263.11
Camp Outside Park	$872.7	6%	$118.94
Other	$779.0	5%	$39.39
Total	$14,712.6	100%	$129

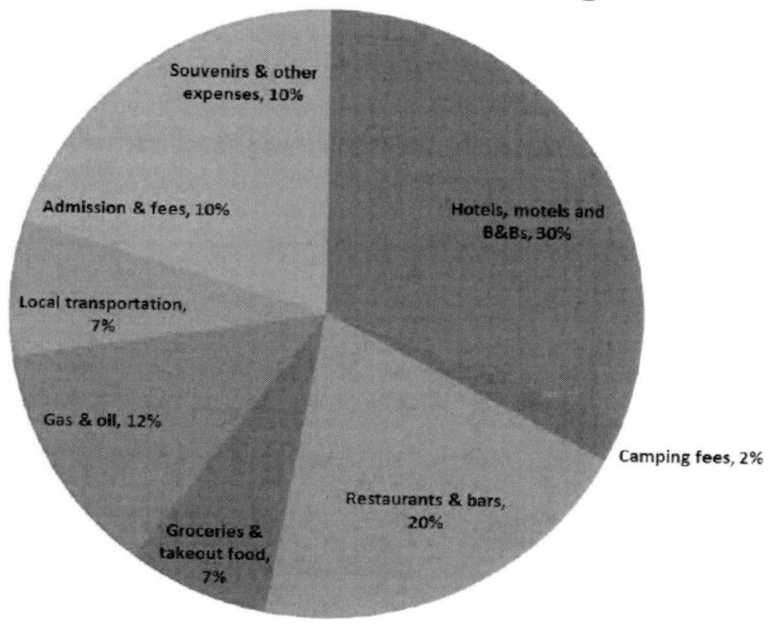

Figure 2. Distribution of NPS visitor spending by spending category. In 2012, visitors to NPS lands spent an estimated $14.7 billion in local gateway communities.

Local Economic Contributions and Impacts of Visitor Spending

This section reports the economic contributions and economic impacts of visitor spending to local gateway economies. These impacts and contributions are an aggregation of park-level effects and use park-level IMPLAN multipliers.

- *Economic contributions* are estimated by multiplying *total (local and nonlocal) visitor spending* by park-level economic multipliers. Table 2 gives the economic contributions to local gateway economies of NPS visitor spending. Individual park-level contribution estimates are included in Table 5 in the appendix. In 2012, NPS visitors spent a total of $14.7 billion in local gateway communities while visiting NPS lands. These expenditures directly supported over 147 thousand jobs, $4.2 billion in labor income, $6.9 billion in value added, and $11.3 billion in output in local gateway economies. The secondary effects of visitor spending supported an additional 54 thousand jobs, $2.5 billion in labor income, $4.4 billion in value added, and $6.9 billion in output. Combined, NPS visitor spending supported a total of 201 thousand jobs, $6.7 billion in labor income, $11.2 billion in value added, and $18.2 billion in output in local gateway economies.
- *Economic impacts* are estimated by multiplying *non-local visitor spending* by park-level economic multipliers. Table 3 gives the economic impacts to local gateway economies of NPS visitor spending. Individual park-level impact estimates are included in Table 6 in the appendix. In 2012, non-local NPS visitors (i.e. visitors who traveled to visit the park from outside of the local gateway region) spent a total of $13.9 billion in local gateway communities while visiting NPS lands. These expenditures directly supported 139 thousand jobs, $4.0 billion in labor income, $6.5 billion in value added, and $10.8 billion in output in local gateway economies. The secondary effects of non-local visitor spending supported an additional 51 thousand jobs, $2.4 billion in labor income, $4.2 billion in value added, and $6.6 billion in output. Combined, non-local NPS visitor spending supported a total of 191 thousand jobs, $6.4 billion in labor income, $10.7 billion in value added, and $17.4 billion in output in local gateway economies.

Table 2. Economic contributions to local gateway economies of NPS visitor spending

Sector	Jobs	Labor Income ($ Millions)	Value Added ($ Millions)	Output ($ Millions)
Direct Effects				
Hotels, motels, and B&Bs	40,076	$1,320.6	$2,510.8	$4,454.6
Camping and other accommodations	4,028	$137.5	$195.4	$358.8
Restaurants and bars	51,213	$1,213.4	$1,730.3	$3,004.9
Grocery and convenience stores	5,179	$163.9	$220.6	$306.3
Gas stations	2,656	$101.3	$152.3	$200.5
Transit and ground transportation services	8,666	$359.4	$685.5	$1,071.1
Other amusement and recreation industries	28,463	$708.6	$1,031.0	$1,490.1
Retail establishments	7,094	$206.4	$330.1	$410.9
Total Direct Effects	147,375	$4,211.1	$6,856.0	$11,297.2
Secondary Effects	53,665	$2,490.1	$4,356.8	$6,939.3
Total Effects	201,040	$6,701.2	$11,212.8	$18,236.5

Table 3. Economic impacts to local gateway economies of NPS visitor spending

Sector	Jobs	Labor Income ($ Millions)	Value Added ($ Millions)	Output ($ Millions)
Direct Effects				
Hotels, motels, and B&Bs	40,076	$1,320.6	$2,510.8	$4,454.6
Camping and other accommodations	4,028	$137.5	$195.4	$358.8
Restaurants and bars	47,182	$1,112.3	$1,585.7	$2,760.0
Grocery and convenience stores	4,512	$141.5	$190.1	$264.7
Gas stations	2,375	$89.3	$134.1	$177.2
Transit and ground transportation services	8,421	$348.6	$665.0	$1,040.2
Other amusement and recreation industries	26,270	$651.9	$950.8	$1,374.5
Retail establishments	6,583	$191.4	$305.9	$380.9
Total Direct Effects	139,447	$3,993.1	$6,537.8	$10,810.9
Secondary Effects	51,460	$2,375.7	$4,156.1	$6,626.5
Total Effects	190,907	$6,368.8	$10,693.9	$17,437.4

National Contribution of Visitor Spending

This section reports the economic contributions of visitors spending to **the national economy**. These contributions are estimated by multiplying total visitor spending by national economic multipliers. Contributions at the national-level are larger than those at the park-level because, as the economic region expands, the amount of secondary spending that stays within that region increases which results in larger economic multipliers.

Table 4 gives the economic contributions to the national economy of NPS visitor spending. In 2012, NPS visitors spent a total of $14.7 billion in local gateway communities while visiting NPS lands. These expenditures directly supported over 145 thousand jobs, $4.2 billion in labor income, $6.9 billion in value added, and $11.3 billion in output in the national economy. The secondary effects of visitor spending supported an additional 97 thousand jobs, $5.1 billion in labor income, $8.9 billion in value added, and $15.5 billion in output in the national economy. Combined, NPS visitor spending supported a total of 242 thousand jobs, $9.3 billion in labor income, $15.8 billion in value added, and $26.8 billion in output in the national economy.

Table 4. Economic contributions to the national economy of NPS visitor spending

Sector	Jobs	Labor Income ($ Millions)	Value Added ($ Millions)	Output ($ Millions)
Direct Effects				
Hotels, motels, and B&Bs	38,707	$1,363.1	$2,577.2	$4,454.6
Camping and other accommodations	3,970	$148.7	$197.7	$358.8
Restaurants and bars	50,741	$1,172.0	$1,701.5	$2,964.3
Grocery and convenience stores	5,200	$162.8	$220.3	$306.3
Gas stations	2,740	$99.8	$150.8	$200.5
Transit and ground transportation services	8,315	$380.2	$725.4	$1,071.3
Other amusement and recreation industries	28,604	$716.8	$1,028.8	$1,490.1
Retail establishments	7,051	$201.6	$330.6	$410.9
Total Direct Effects	145,328	$4,245.0	$6,932.3	$11,256.8
Secondary Effects	97,384	$5,102.3	$8,876.9	$15,497.3
Total Effects	242,712	$9,347.0	$15,809.0	$26,754.0

State and Regional Contributions

Impacts to state and regional economies are provided in the appendix in Tables 7 and 8. State-level contributions use state-level IMPLAN models and regional-level contributions use regional IMPLAN models. For parks that fall within multiple states, park spending is proportionally allocated to each state based on the share of park visits that occur within each state. Visit shares for multi-state parks are listed in Table 9 in the appendix.

The size of the region included in an IMPLAN model influences the magnitude of the economic multiplier effects. As the economic region expands, the amount of secondary spending that stays within that region increases, which results in larger economic multipliers. Thus, contributions at the national level are larger than those at the regional, state, and local levels.

Limitations

The accuracy of spending and impact estimates rests largely on the input data, namely (1) public use recreation visit and overnight stay data; (2) party size, length of stay, and park re-entry conversion factors; (3) visitor segment shares; (4) spending averages; and (5) local area multipliers.

Public use data provide estimates of visitor entries for most parks. Various counting instructions consider travel mode context at park units to derive recreation and non-recreation visitation at both a monthly and annual resolution. Re-entry factors, vehicle occupancy rates and other corrections are collected using travel surveys that increase the accuracy of these estimates. System audits regularly occur to ensure quality control for the automated equipment and regularity of park staff collected information. While these methods are well established in the visitor use estimation literature, these are still estimates.

Visitor spending estimates are calculated by multiplying total party days/nights for each visitor segment by average spending profiles for each visitor segment. Accurate estimates of visitor segment splits and trip characteristic data, including park re-entry rates, party sizes, and lengths of stay in the area, are needed to convert park visits to the number of party days/nights by visitor segment. As with the MGM2 model, data used in the VSE model are derived from Visitor Services Project (VSP) surveys. Exactly how VSP data was extrapolated from surveyed parks to represent non-surveyed parks in the MGM2 model is not clearly documented; thus, the processes used for this analysis could not be matched to those used in the MGM2. As a result, park-bypark spending and trip characteristic data used in the VSE model differ from those used in the MGM2 model. Because of this change in the underlying visitor data, park-by-park visitor spending estimates from this year's analysis are not directly comparable to previous analyses.

For each park, visitors are split into seven visitor segments (local day trip, non-local day trip, NPS lodge, NPS campground, motel outside park, camp outside park, and other). Visitor segment splits for each park determine how many visits are attributed to each visitor segment, and can have a substantial effect on visitor spending estimates. As with trip characteristic data, visitor segment splits are derived from VSP data. These data seem to overestimate the percent of visits that fall into the 'other' segment. 'Other' visitors are defined as non-local visitors who stay overnight in the local region but do not have any lodging expenses. This segment includes visitors staying in private homes, with friends or relatives, or in other unpaid lodging. Although the percent of visits assigned to this segment is likely overestimated, average spending for the 'other' segment is low; thus, an overestimate in the percent of visits that are classified as 'other' should have a downward effect on spending and economic effect estimates.

Many visitors come to local gateway regions primarily to visit NPS lands. However, some visitors are primarily in the area for business, visiting friends and relatives, or for some other reason, and their visit to a NPS unit is not their primary purpose for their trip. For these visitors, it may not be appropriate to attribute all of their trip expenditures to the NPS. The VSE model only counts expenditures for the number of days that these visitors visit the park, but it does not adjust daily expenditures to omit spending such as motel and rental car expenses. This likely results in an over-attribution of visitor spending in sectors such as lodging and local transportation. Future versions of the VSE model will improve this methodology as better data on trip purpose and visitor spending become available.

The generic profiles constructed from the available VSP data should be reasonably accurate for many park units. However, a number of parks are not well represented by the generic visitor spending and trip characteristic profiles developed from the VSP data. For these parks, profiles were constructed using the best available data. These units include parks in Alaska, parks in the Washington D.C. area, parkways, and parks in highly urban areas. There is a great need for increased sampling rigor across park types and geographic regions in order to increase the accuracy of these data and thus improve the accuracy of future visitor spending effects analyses. Efforts are underway to diversify the number of park units that these profiles represent. It is expected that these inputs to the model will continue to improve, and park unit specific data will be more prevalent through socioeconomic monitoring.

Parks in Alaska

Visit characteristics and spending at Alaska parks are unique. Spending opportunities near Alaska parks are limited and for many visitors a park visit is part of a cruise or guided tour, frequently purchased as a package. Most visitors are on extended trips to Alaska, making it difficult to allocate expenses to a particular park visit. Lodging, vehicle rentals, and air expenses frequently occur in Anchorage, many miles from the park. Also, many Alaska parks are only accessible by air or boat, so spending profiles estimated from visitor surveys at parks in the lower 48 states do not apply well. For this analysis, Alaska statewide multipliers are used to estimate impacts for parks in Alaska. Visitor trip characteristics and spending profiles are adopted from two reports on visitor spending and impacts in Alaska: a 2010 report on visitor spending and economic significance of visitation to Katmai National Park and Preserve (Fay and Christensen, 2010), and a 2010 report on the economic impacts of visitors to southeast Alaska (McDowell Group, 2010). Based on these new profiles, visitor spending estimates for the Alaska region are up from $237 million in 2011 to $1.1 billion in 2012. Although much higher, the new Alaska profiles are based on Alaska specific data and we feel that the increases are warranted. A 2008 report from the University of Alaska Anchorage described the economic impacts of various industries within the Alaskan Gross State Product (GSP), and discussed the importance of the tourism industry to the State (Goldsmith, 2008). GSP of Alaska was $51.9 billion in 2012 (BEA, 2013), and our estimates show a value-added to the Alaskan economy from park visitation of $890 million in 2012, or about 1.5 percent of GSP. A recent report by the U.S. Travel Association estimated that travelers to Alaska created 26,000 jobs from spending $2.2 billion in 2011 (USTA, 2013). Comparatively, visitation to National Park units in Alaska are calculated to contribute 16 thousand jobs. These comparisons indicate that the economic effects resulting from visitation to National Park units, although greatly increased from previous estimates, represent a reasonable estimated contribution to the Alaskan tourism industry and economy as a whole.

Parks in the Washington D.C. Area

The many monuments and parks in the Washington, D.C. area each count visitors separately. To avoid double counting of spending across many national capital parks, we must know how many times a visitor has been counted at park units during a trip to the Washington, D.C. area. For parks in the Washington, D.C. area, we assume an average of 1.7 park visits are counted for day trips by local visitors, 3.4 visits for day trips by non-local visitors, and 5.1 park visits on overnight trips (Stynes, 2011). Better data on visitor trip patterns in the Washington D.C. area would improve the accuracy of spending and economic effects for these parks.

Parkways and Urban Parks

Parkways and urban parks present special difficulties for economic impact analyses. These units have some of the highest number of visits while posing the most difficult problems for estimating visits, spending, and impacts. The majority of visits to these types of units were assumed to be day trips by local or non-local visitors. Due to the high numbers of visits at these units, small changes in assumed spending averages or segment mixes can swing the spending estimates by substantial amounts. Better data on parkway and urban park spending patterns and trip characteristics are needed.

References

Bureau of Economic Analysis (BEA). 2013. BEARFACTS, Gross Domestic Product (GDP) by State. Available at: http://www.bea.gov/regional/bearfacts/action.cfm?geoType=3&fips=02000&areatype=02000.

Fay, G. and Christensen, J., 2010. Katmai National Park and Preserve Economic Significance Analysis and Model Documentation. Prepared for: National Park Conservation Association and National Park Service, Katmai National Park and Preserve, 60 pp.

Goldsmith, S. 2008. What Drives the Alaska Economy? University of Alaska Anchorage, Institute of Social and Economic Research. UA Research Summary, Number 3.

IMPLAN Group LLC, IMPLAN System (data and software), 16740 Birkdale Commons Parkway Suite 206, Huntersville, NC 28078 www.implan.com

McDowell Group, 2010. Economic Impact of Visitors to Southeast Alaska, 2010-11. Prepared for: Alaska Wilderness League, 33 pp.

Street, B. 2013. Statistical abstract: 2012. Natural Resource Data Series NPS/NRSS/EQD/NRDS—2013/473. National Park Service, Fort Collins, Colorado.

Stynes, D. J. 2011. Economic Benefits to Local Communities from National Park Visitation and Payroll, 2010. Natural Resource Report NPS/NRSS/EQD/NRR—2011/481. National Park Service, Fort Collins, Colorado.

U.S. Travel Association (USTA). 2013. Travel in an Economic Engine, Why Travel Matters to Alaska. Available at: http://traveleffect.com/sites/travel effect.com/files/states/Travel_Impact_AK.pdf.

APPENDIX

Table 5. Visits, spending and economic contributions to local economies of NPS visitors spending

Park Unit	Total Recreation Visits	Total Visitor Spending ($000s)	Contribution of all Visitor Spending			
			Jobs	Labor Income ($000s)	Value Added ($000s)	Output ($000s)
Abraham Lincoln Birthplace NHP	169,515	$9,121.8	137	$3,942.9	$6,781.6	$11,529.9
Acadia NP	2,431,052	$200,920.0	3,089	$92,344.3	$152,518.7	$264,000.6
Adams NHP	336,031	$18,082.2	244	$9,443.3	$15,317.3	$23,901.9
African Burial Ground NM	77,624	$4,177.0	48	$2,268.1	$3,670.3	$5,365.3
Agate Fossil Beds NM*	11,824	$798.9	10	$216.1	$405.0	$770.8
Alibates Flint Quarries NM	3,383	$182.0	3	$59.5	$117.6	$206.0
Allegheny Portage Railroad NHS	138,864	$7,472.4	113	$3,336.0	$5,511.0	$9,409.4
Amistad NRA	1,367,502	$54,971.7	689	$14,877.9	$29,549.7	$51,611.8
Andersonville NHS	122,883	$6,612.5	99	$2,250.3	$4,162.3	$7,471.5
Andrew Johnson NHS	51,261	$2,758.4	40	$1,121.2	$1,947.6	$3,319.3
Aniakchak NM&PRES	19	$28.9	0	$14.4	$24.3	$40.3
Antietam NB	510,921	$27,493.3	361	$14,004.1	$22,634.2	$35,085.0
Apostle Islands NL*	163,419	$24,030.6	330	$7,686.0	$14,999.5	$25,991.0
Appomattox Court House NHP	320,668	$17,255.5	249	$6,396.0	$11,378.1	$19,666.4
Arches NP*	1,070,577	$115,859.9	1,708	$44,827.1	$79,851.3	$138,019.2
Arkansas Post NMEM	39,703	$2,353.4	31	$976.4	$1,596.7	$2,700.3
Arlington House, The Robert E. Lee Memorial NMEM	562,772	$30,283.4	393	$15,509.8	$25,057.6	$38,581.6
Assateague Island NS	2,154,859	$86,309.3	1,087	$29,752.7	$53,772.2	$89,381.0
Aztec Ruins NM	44,744	$2,407.7	33	$800.0	$1,394.8	$2,466.1

Table 5. (Continued)

Park Unit	Total Recreation Visits	Total Visitor Spending ($000s)	Contribution of all Visitor Spending			
			Jobs	Labor Income ($000s)	Value Added ($000s)	Output ($000s)
Badlands NP	883,406	$52,145.4	779	$18,171.1	$32,877.0	$60,151.2
Bandelier NM	150,289	$8,711.8	125	$3,642.6	$6,031.8	$10,428.0
Bent's Old Fort NHS	25,815	$1,389.1	19	$530.1	$921.9	$1,555.0
Bering Land Bridge NPRES	2,642	$3,816.1	53	$1,906.4	$3,201.2	$5,313.8
Big Bend NP	292,055	$24,230.1	322	$7,045.5	$14,489.8	$25,089.9
Big Cypress NPRES	882,570	$64,229.1	853	$33,714.4	$55,979.7	$88,182.4
Big Hole NB	35,207	$1,894.5	28	$681.6	$1,098.1	$2,027.1
Big South Fork NRRA*	600,161	$16,923.0	213	$5,640.0	$9,921.6	$16,773.5
Big Thicket NPRES	135,262	$7,962.7	99	$3,506.8	$5,984.1	$9,558.2
Bighorn Canyon NRA	245,831	$9,821.1	140	$3,626.7	$5,993.8	$10,738.0
Biscayne NP	495,613	$29,193.6	376	$15,120.0	$24,668.0	$38,549.6
Black Canyon Of The Gunnison NP	192,570	$11,027.6	133	$4,624.3	$7,447.9	$11,998.7
Blue Ridge PKWY	15,205,059	$902,472.1	12,168	$425,173.7	$724,544.1	$1,157,425.0
Bluestone NSR	36,842	$1,463.4	19	$514.6	$866.2	$1,485.8
Booker T Washington NM	24,361	$1,310.9	19	$508.2	$880.6	$1,517.3
Boston NHP	2,629,064	$141,473.1	1,916	$74,143.1	$120,015.9	$187,426.8
Boston African American NHS	404,248	$21,753.1	295	$11,391.3	$18,447.8	$28,818.0
Brown V Board Of Education NHS	21,101	$1,135.5	18	$562.5	$916.7	$1,551.5
Bryce Canyon NP	1,385,352	$108,946.2	1,501	$40,402.4	$72,634.8	$125,121.3
Buck Island Reef NM	30,436	$1,727.1	20	$777.6	$1,318.4	$2,028.7
Buffalo NR	1,093,083	$43,789.7	610	$15,325.2	$26,366.8	$46,933.1
Cabrillo NM	877,951	$47,243.6	597	$22,379.0	$36,275.7	$56,547.2
Canaveral NS	994,430	$58,891.6	785	$26,758.3	$46,216.4	$74,220.5
Cane River Creole NHP	28,310	$1,523.4	21	$555.1	$1,010.9	$1,741.7
Canyon De Chelly NM	828,523	$50,552.4	667	$15,857.6	$28,619.8	$51,794.6
Canyonlands NP	452,952	$25,208.9	338	$9,027.6	$16,018.6	$27,739.8
Cape Cod NS	4,441,290	$179,053.0	2,170	$88,236.2	$138,308.4	$212,833.2
Cape Hatteras NS	2,302,040	$135,055.5	1,884	$52,131.9	$90,726.3	$154,392.3
Cape Krusenstern NM	24,950	$36,037.8	502	$18,003.3	$30,231.0	$50,181.6
Cape Lookout NS	480,294	$20,883.9	297	$6,695.6	$11,889.2	$21,367.4
Capitol Reef NP*	673,345	$44,636.7	554	$15,085.1	$26,928.0	$47,353.9
Capulin Volcano NM*	48,710	$1,353.6	19	$351.1	$657.6	$1,210.7
Carl Sandburg Home NHS	93,429	$5,027.5	74	$2,011.2	$3,452.9	$5,923.3
Carlsbad Caverns NP	381,058	$22,584.7	296	$7,256.0	$12,584.3	$22,714.9
Casa Grande Ruins NM	68,631	$3,693.1	53	$1,906.3	$3,099.5	$4,985.5
Castillo De San Marcos NM	727,243	$39,133.8	557	$17,006.2	$29,910.9	$48,961.7
Castle Clinton NM	3,264,439	$75,371.0	802	$35,064.5	$55,142.6	$80,629.1
Catoctin Mountain P	263,797	$15,092.8	191	$7,540.8	$12,269.6	$19,078.7
Cedar Breaks NM	631,809	$37,415.5	499	$13,189.1	$23,603.3	$40,989.6

Park Unit	Total Recreation Visits	Total Visitor Spending ($000s)	Contribution of all Visitor Spending			
			Jobs	Labor Income ($000s)	Value Added ($000s)	Output ($000s)
Chaco Culture NHP	39,044	$2,255.3	32	$892.5	$1,508.4	$2,633.6
Chamizal NMEM	104,148	$5,604.3	79	$2,022.8	$3,754.8	$6,513.6
Channel Islands NP	249,594	$13,997.1	178	$7,325.1	$11,846.0	$18,712.5
Charles Pinckney NHS	44,314	$2,384.6	34	$1,016.5	$1,682.3	$2,798.6
Chattahoochee River NRA	3,168,137	$125,842.2	1,775	$62,089.0	$100,423.4	$163,725.0
Chesapeake & Ohio Canal NHP	4,712,377	$81,886.2	1,117	$41,793.4	$69,281.1	$108,949.3
Chickamauga & Chattanooga NMP	1,032,844	$61,166.5	867	$21,428.2	$39,092.9	$69,309.5
Chickasaw NRA*	1,487,039	$22,135.6	213	$5,096.4	$8,614.6	$15,030.3
Chiricahua NM	41,159	$2,322.0	29	$695.9	$1,281.8	$2,263.7
Christiansted NHS	126,962	$6,832.0	82	$3,189.0	$5,307.0	$8,199.6
City Of Rocks NRES	98,996	$5,327.1	74	$1,936.3	$3,242.2	$5,679.6
Clara Barton NHS	25,347	$1,364.0	18	$698.2	$1,128.2	$1,738.8
Colonial NHP	3,274,187	$176,187.9	2,539	$74,263.3	$127,177.5	$213,797.7
Colorado NM	454,510	$26,577.4	356	$9,626.7	$17,086.4	$29,307.6
Congaree NP*	109,685	$5,144.0	66	$1,875.7	$3,235.6	$5,556.7
Coronado NMEM	97,579	$5,250.8	72	$2,093.2	$3,529.4	$5,910.4
Cowpens NB	231,973	$13,750.4	201	$6,323.6	$10,595.8	$17,889.2
Crater Lake NP	447,251	$36,097.0	551	$15,597.4	$25,714.4	$45,060.0
Craters Of The Moon NM&PRES*	197,529	$6,334.6	91	$2,021.0	$3,512.6	$6,615.1
Cumberland Gap NHP	853,998	$50,370.3	702	$19,481.0	$34,973.5	$59,905.5
Cumberland Island NS	61,493	$2,390.0	32	$1,009.3	$1,688.0	$2,761.8
Curecanti NRA	862,612	$34,458.3	414	$13,338.2	$21,560.8	$35,130.6
Cuyahoga Valley NP	2,299,722	$136,751.8	2,054	$59,054.4	$101,681.8	$175,232.8
Dayton Aviation Heritage NHP*	65,999	$3,581.8	60	$1,827.3	$3,055.2	$5,210.2
De Soto NMEM	432,981	$23,299.2	332	$11,342.4	$19,330.3	$31,123.9
Death Valley NP	984,568	$77,966.6	929	$35,665.6	$59,370.8	$91,346.0
Delaware Water Gap NRA*	4,970,802	$156,372.2	2,319	$98,007.6	$149,653.1	$216,180.1
Denali NP&PRES	388,433	$371,501.1	5,098	$185,911.3	$313,678.5	$520,780.6
Devils Postpile NM	87,845	$5,127.9	65	$1,910.7	$3,442.8	$5,754.4
Devils Tower NM	416,994	$24,517.8	352	$8,581.0	$15,349.7	$27,700.0
Dinosaur NM	302,858	$16,936.9	201	$6,142.5	$10,240.8	$17,109.2
Dry Tortugas NP	60,550	$3,210.6	33	$1,241.3	$2,067.6	$3,221.1
Edgar Allan Poe NHS	19,104	$1,028.0	14	$554.6	$879.4	$1,405.5
Effigy Mounds NM*	78,540	$4,603.6	68	$1,655.2	$2,866.0	$5,131.2
Eisenhower NHS	53,286	$2,867.4	38	$1,457.6	$2,344.0	$3,644.3
El Malpais NM	114,678	$6,797.4	98	$2,727.9	$4,641.4	$8,132.2
El Morro NM	44,808	$2,609.3	36	$647.1	$1,295.7	$2,465.3
Eleanor Roosevelt NHS	55,049	$2,962.3	36	$1,409.0	$2,404.6	$3,606.7
Eugene O'Neill NHS	2,789	$150.1	2	$80.0	$125.0	$194.9
Everglades NP	1,141,906	$102,764.6	1,402	$56,736.8	$94,038.6	$147,065.1
Federal Hall NMEM	167,146	$8,994.3	103	$4,897.3	$7,900.4	$11,537.4

Table 5. (Continued)

Park Unit	Total Recreation Visits	Total Visitor Spending ($000s)	Contribution of all Visitor Spending			
			Jobs	Labor Income ($000s)	Value Added ($000s)	Output ($000s)
Fire Island NS	483,334	$19,258.5	206	$9,805.5	$15,702.4	$22,852.3
First Ladies NHS	9,903	$532.9	8	$251.2	$416.0	$705.1
Flight 93 NMEM	317,926	$17,108.0	258	$7,631.3	$12,646.0	$21,557.0
Florissant Fossil Beds NM	62,637	$3,370.6	47	$1,781.2	$2,809.0	$4,493.5
Ford's Theatre NHS	701,542	$12,209.0	161	$6,424.6	$10,535.9	$16,244.2
Fort Bowie NHS	7,966	$428.7	6	$168.6	$284.0	$476.4
Fort Caroline NMEM	327,339	$17,614.5	252	$8,032.7	$13,818.7	$22,559.2
Fort Davis NHS	38,136	$2,052.1	27	$562.0	$1,149.7	$2,013.0
Fort Donelson NB	284,762	$16,878.1	226	$7,587.5	$12,572.9	$20,522.8
Fort Frederica NM	262,235	$14,111.2	196	$6,238.1	$10,501.0	$17,209.5
Fort Laramie NHS	55,199	$2,970.3	40	$1,001.1	$1,803.6	$3,173.0
Fort Larned NHS*	33,194	$1,852.8	24	$538.6	$1,032.4	$1,916.0
Fort Matanzas NM	497,574	$26,775.1	378	$11,612.1	$20,389.2	$33,214.1
Fort McHenry NM&SHRINE	744,076	$40,039.6	526	$20,475.9	$33,345.8	$51,649.7
Fort Necessity NB	187,893	$11,126.4	162	$5,047.2	$8,402.5	$14,244.6
Fort Point NHS	1,502,786	$80,866.7	999	$43,119.0	$67,373.6	$105,104.1
Fort Pulaski NM	385,751	$22,865.5	307	$9,303.5	$15,748.9	$26,189.7
Fort Raleigh NHS	281,833	$15,165.8	221	$5,976.0	$10,288.9	$17,524.8
Fort Scott NHS*	25,034	$414.5	5	$107.5	$189.6	$349.5
Fort Smith NHS	87,386	$4,702.3	70	$1,671.2	$2,962.9	$5,357.2
Fort Stanwix NM*	195,057	$9,841.4	117	$3,189.1	$7,058.3	$11,200.7
Fort Sumter NM	842,027	$45,310.3	650	$19,283.4	$31,980.2	$53,245.9
Fort Union NM*	9,215	$572.7	7	$213.9	$342.9	$583.9
Fort Union Trading Post NHS*	12,677	$937.1	10	$279.4	$451.6	$772.4
Fort Vancouver NHS	681,404	$36,667.2	559	$17,831.3	$28,965.7	$49,366.5
Fort Washington P	368,824	$19,846.9	254	$10,183.8	$16,417.8	$25,151.5
Fossil Butte NM*	17,084	$786.9	9	$258.6	$436.4	$740.5
Franklin Delano Roosevelt MEM	2,764,459	$48,110.3	636	$25,316.5	$41,517.4	$64,011.2
Frederick Douglass NHS	53,314	$927.8	12	$489.0	$801.0	$1,233.1
Frederick Law Olmsted NHS	8,668	$466.4	6	$243.4	$395.5	$617.9
Fredericksburg & Spotsylvania NMP	982,324	$52,860.0	673	$26,489.8	$42,462.0	$65,469.7
Friendship Hill NHS	34,289	$1,845.1	28	$844.1	$1,390.3	$2,348.7
Gates Of The Arctic NP&PRES	10,899	$15,742.5	219	$7,864.4	$13,205.9	$21,921.0
Gateway NRA	5,043,863	$116,410.1	1,261	$54,718.5	$85,632.9	$126,142.7
Gauley River NRA	115,283	$4,613.8	61	$1,658.5	$2,725.6	$4,691.5
General Grant NMEM	92,418	$4,973.1	57	$2,700.2	$4,372.2	$6,393.7
George Rogers Clark NHP	125,972	$6,778.7	99	$2,321.8	$4,282.7	$7,619.8

Park Unit	Total Recreation Visits	Total Visitor Spending ($000s)	Contribution of all Visitor Spending			
			Jobs	Labor Income ($000s)	Value Added ($000s)	Output ($000s)
George Washington MEM PKWY	7,425,577	$44,720.7	747	$24,587.0	$37,324.5	$58,080.3
George Washington Birthplace NM*	134,824	$5,663.9	70	$2,792.4	$4,444.6	$6,832.9
George Washington Carver NM*	30,425	$518.5	7	$175.3	$294.2	$519.5
Gettysburg NMP	1,126,577	$66,317.6	838	$32,999.2	$53,764.7	$83,831.3
Gila Cliff Dwellings NM	28,637	$1,541.0	22	$399.9	$775.8	$1,457.4
Glacier NP	2,162,035	$172,420.9	2,754	$74,203.6	$120,092.1	$218,224.4
Glacier Bay NP&PRES	454,337	$92,676.3	1,661	$49,742.6	$77,034.6	$121,675.5
Glen Canyon NRA	2,061,328	$114,888.1	1,436	$39,140.3	$68,381.6	$117,506.6
Golden Gate NRA	14,540,338	$337,853.1	3,722	$152,599.9	$236,608.0	$364,463.0
Golden Spike NHS*	42,551	$2,246.0	32	$976.7	$1,613.9	$2,813.1
Governors Island NM	348,249	$18,739.7	216	$10,203.5	$16,460.4	$24,038.2
Grand Canyon NP*	4,421,352	$453,641.3	6,010	$225,593.2	$381,343.5	$574,714.9
Grand Portage NM	93,156	$5,518.0	72	$1,410.8	$2,906.1	$5,227.0
Grand Teton NP*	2,705,256	$454,093.6	6,339	$187,916.8	$307,522.1	$539,345.1
Grant-Kohrs Ranch NHS	17,095	$919.9	15	$405.1	$630.8	$1,139.8
Great Basin NP	94,850	$4,912.6	60	$1,394.6	$2,588.9	$4,562.5
Great Sand Dunes NP&PRES	254,674	$14,323.0	188	$5,300.5	$9,288.2	$15,808.5
Great Smoky Mountains NP	9,685,829	$741,499.1	10,959	$322,195.7	$561,629.6	$951,891.4
Greenbelt P	145,552	$8,353.6	103	$4,170.7	$6,809.4	$10,473.5
Guadalupe Mountains NP	159,360	$9,111.5	121	$3,148.7	$5,858.0	$10,084.4
Guilford Courthouse NMP	313,374	$18,575.4	272	$8,252.8	$13,810.3	$23,489.1
Gulf Islands NS	4,973,462	$199,385.0	2,671	$81,202.1	$136,305.6	$226,010.5
Hagerman Fossil Beds NM	23,936	$1,288.0	19	$562.8	$896.2	$1,543.2
Haleakala NP	1,094,668	$64,461.3	736	$29,322.9	$49,742.1	$76,554.9
Hamilton Grange NMEM	16,358	$880.2	10	$477.4	$773.0	$1,128.5
Hampton NHS	37,529	$2,019.5	27	$1,040.5	$1,688.2	$2,619.5
Harpers Ferry NHP*	263,105	$11,929.2	168	$6,537.1	$10,468.6	$16,171.3
Harry S Truman NHS	31,316	$1,685.2	27	$849.6	$1,376.2	$2,337.1
Hawaii Volcanoes NP	1,483,928	$113,376.4	1,353	$53,242.9	$91,775.8	$140,542.1
Herbert Hoover NHS	128,812	$6,931.5	104	$2,661.5	$4,708.3	$8,301.7
Home Of Franklin D Roosevelt NHS	135,746	$7,304.7	88	$3,540.0	$5,980.1	$8,956.3
Homestead NM*	103,708	$3,158.2	42	$985.6	$1,738.1	$3,190.2
Hopewell Culture NHP	39,462	$2,123.5	32	$981.2	$1,637.3	$2,782.5
Hopewell Furnace NHS	52,870	$2,845.0	41	$1,478.5	$2,385.9	$3,888.2
Horseshoe Bend NMP	58,668	$3,157.0	47	$1,362.6	$2,238.8	$3,889.0
Hot Springs NP	1,302,505	$77,011.2	1,106	$31,306.0	$54,049.2	$94,543.3
Hovenweep NM	26,710	$1,554.5	20	$538.7	$940.5	$1,631.9
Hubbell Trading Post NHS	75,061	$4,039.1	55	$1,277.9	$2,269.9	$4,097.0
Independence NHP	3,594,549	$193,427.0	2,720	$104,349.4	$165,458.2	$264,450.7
Indiana Dunes NL	1,889,381	$75,915.5	947	$37,017.9	$62,529.5	$97,244.2
Isle Royale NP	16,663	$3,477.1	50	$1,155.8	$2,185.9	$3,777.4

Table 5. (Continued)

Park Unit	Total Recreation Visits	Total Visitor Spending ($000s)	Contribution of all Visitor Spending			
			Jobs	Labor Income ($000s)	Value Added ($000s)	Output ($000s)
James A Garfield NHS*	36,375	$1,195.8	20	$545.5	$922.5	$1,598.4
Jean Lafitte NP&PRES	419,694	$22,584.2	317	$9,848.9	$16,564.7	$27,551.2
Jefferson NEM*	2,496,726	$228,290.7	3,883	$121,147.2	$200,565.4	$337,531.7
Jewel Cave NM	109,300	$5,881.6	89	$2,075.2	$3,713.2	$6,719.4
Jimmy Carter NHS	69,940	$3,763.6	56	$1,278.9	$2,359.4	$4,234.9
John D Rockefeller Jr MEM PKWY	1,197,750	$37,898.5	586	$18,704.0	$30,950.2	$58,143.3
John Day Fossil Beds NM*	148,152	$6,493.6	88	$2,329.9	$3,875.8	$7,094.2
John F Kennedy NHS	22,642	$1,218.4	17	$635.3	$1,032.9	$1,614.0
John Muir NHS	37,403	$2,012.7	25	$1,072.5	$1,677.1	$2,618.0
Johnstown Flood NMEM*	123,081	$6,977.7	116	$3,318.5	$5,476.5	$9,383.4
Joshua Tree NP*	1,396,117	$62,175.8	770	$29,200.4	$48,440.6	$76,465.1
Kalaupapa NHP	58,875	$3,168.1	38	$1,478.8	$2,461.0	$3,802.3
Kaloko-Honokohau NHP	153,584	$8,264.5	99	$3,857.7	$6,419.9	$9,918.9
Katmai NP&PRES	39,818	$57,513.1	801	$28,731.7	$48,246.1	$80,085.3
Kenai Fjords NP	281,279	$52,487.9	965	$28,359.6	$43,509.5	$68,349.9
Kennesaw Mountain NBP	1,935,909	$104,173.6	1,556	$54,963.0	$89,439.0	$145,587.8
Kings Canyon NP	591,033	$45,904.3	605	$18,239.2	$32,447.3	$53,903.4
Kings Mountain NMP*	265,713	$9,800.7	139	$4,373.8	$7,293.8	$12,329.6
Klondike Gold Rush NHP Alaska	854,250	$160,289.5	2,942	$86,568.5	$132,894.4	$208,840.2
Klondike Gold Rush NHP Washington	60,198	$3,239.3	40	$1,444.5	$2,607.9	$4,051.0
Knife River Indian Villages NHS	16,010	$861.5	12	$317.5	$564.3	$988.4
Kobuk Valley NP	29,550	$42,682.0	595	$21,322.5	$35,804.7	$59,433.5
Korean War Veterans MEM	3,267,124	$56,858.2	751	$29,919.8	$49,066.5	$75,650.5
Lake Chelan NRA	40,830	$1,886.4	21	$817.2	$1,442.4	$2,215.3
Lake Clark NP&PRES	11,639	$16,811.4	234	$8,398.4	$14,102.6	$23,409.3
Lake Mead NRA	6,285,439	$252,209.9	2,840	$104,434.5	$168,932.0	$260,093.3
Lake Meredith NRA	502,457	$20,120.2	275	$6,300.5	$12,112.6	$21,258.4
Lake Roosevelt NRA	1,781,972	$71,589.9	899	$24,701.4	$47,708.4	$78,176.8
Lassen Volcanic NP	407,653	$22,918.1	297	$7,454.3	$14,242.3	$24,684.1
Lava Beds NM*	181,429	$7,152.0	86	$2,315.7	$3,995.1	$6,924.5
Lewis and Clark NHP	201,704	$10,853.9	153	$4,859.3	$8,118.9	$13,534.6
Lincoln MEM	6,191,361	$107,749.1	1,424	$56,699.5	$92,983.5	$143,361.3
Lincoln Boyhood NMEM*	133,550	$5,840.2	93	$2,637.0	$4,455.8	$7,564.8
Lincoln Home NHS*	295,464	$16,467.3	214	$5,398.6	$11,357.6	$18,776.6
Little Bighorn Battlefield NM	346,327	$18,636.3	288	$7,525.4	$12,169.7	$21,986.2
Little River Canyon NPRES	201,109	$10,821.9	160	$4,233.3	$7,392.0	$12,776.2
Little Rock Central High School NHS	63,938	$3,440.6	52	$1,447.7	$2,470.1	$4,318.1

Park Unit	Total Recreation Visits	Total Visitor Spending ($000s)	Contribution of all Visitor Spending			
			Jobs	Labor Income ($000s)	Value Added ($000s)	Output ($000s)
Longfellow NHS	52,234	$2,810.8	38	$1,471.4	$2,384.6	$3,726.9
Lowell NHP	537,551	$28,926.3	397	$15,116.8	$24,472.3	$38,408.5
Lyndon B Johnson NHP	110,791	$5,961.8	84	$2,685.8	$4,677.3	$7,613.1
Lyndon Baines Johnson Memorial Grove on the Potomac NMEM	371,063	$19,967.3	259	$10,226.4	$16,521.7	$25,438.8
Maggie L Walker NHS	8,276	$445.3	6	$183.7	$317.6	$533.2
Mammoth Cave NP	508,054	$40,429.6	574	$19,154.1	$31,708.2	$51,977.1
Manassas NBP	600,354	$32,305.8	416	$16,546.9	$26,687.2	$41,012.0
Manzanar NHS*	72,831	$6,992.9	86	$2,533.4	$4,545.0	$7,628.4
Marsh - Billings - Rockefeller NHP	32,403	$1,743.6	24	$719.8	$1,261.3	$2,057.3
Martin Luther King Jr NHS	707,514	$38,072.2	569	$20,278.6	$32,931.6	$53,501.1
Martin Luther King, Jr. MEM	3,738,336	$65,058.8	860	$34,235.1	$56,143.3	$86,561.4
Martin Van Buren NHS	22,062	$1,187.2	15	$511.3	$929.4	$1,426.3
Mary McLeod Bethune Council House NHS	6,646	$115.7	2	$60.9	$99.8	$153.9
Mesa Verde NP*	488,860	$46,696.1	645	$17,011.2	$29,839.6	$51,561.0
Minute Man NHP	1,001,207	$53,876.2	735	$28,210.1	$45,739.9	$71,633.4
Minuteman Missile NHS*	75,654	$5,173.3	77	$1,773.3	$3,281.8	$6,058.0
Mississippi NRRA	106,733	$4,239.6	60	$1,893.4	$3,266.6	$5,445.8
Missouri NRR	167,776	$6,664.3	98	$2,276.3	$3,999.2	$7,360.8
Mojave NPRES	542,527	$29,176.0	354	$13,178.3	$21,573.7	$33,325.4
Monocacy NB*	47,249	$3,622.3	46	$1,866.1	$3,062.6	$4,750.6
Montezuma Castle NM	455,305	$24,500.5	347	$12,464.1	$20,151.8	$32,108.9
Moores Creek NB	79,345	$4,683.4	65	$1,645.3	$3,000.1	$5,178.7
Morristown NHP	294,606	$15,853.1	188	$8,721.3	$14,000.0	$20,696.6
Mount Rainier NP*	1,049,178	$36,843.8	432	$15,817.3	$28,461.7	$43,999.7
Mount Rushmore NMEM	2,185,447	$117,601.5	1,815	$42,523.7	$75,945.0	$137,371.4
Muir Woods NM	972,331	$52,322.3	641	$27,808.2	$43,339.4	$67,292.5
Natchez NHP	184,551	$9,930.9	138	$3,854.2	$6,584.8	$11,333.4
Natchez Trace PKWY	5,560,668	$125,966.2	1,550	$40,892.4	$67,819.1	$110,944.9
National Capital Parks Central	858,700	$14,944.1	198	$7,858.0	$12,894.5	$19,901.3
National Capital Parks East	923,054	$16,064.0	217	$8,409.9	$13,941.1	$21,686.4
National Park of American Samoa	10,440	$561.8	7	$262.2	$436.4	$674.2
Natural Bridges NM	89,011	$5,140.6	64	$1,720.5	$3,041.4	$5,213.1
Navajo NM	58,219	$3,398.0	42	$1,142.2	$2,015.2	$3,449.6
New Bedford Whaling NHP*	269,885	$13,297.4	193	$7,263.3	$11,748.5	$18,023.3
New Orleans Jazz NHP	177,909	$9,573.5	135	$4,358.4	$7,211.7	$11,872.7
New River Gorge NR	1,128,195	$45,344.2	605	$16,133.0	$27,202.8	$46,901.4
Nez Perce NHP	233,093	$12,543.0	176	$4,432.4	$8,564.8	$14,511.4
Nicodemus NHS*	3,505	$181.6	2	$45.0	$87.8	$156.4
Ninety Six NHS	73,044	$3,930.6	58	$1,539.9	$2,694.3	$4,674.1

Table 5. (Continued)

Park Unit	Total Recreation Visits	Total Visitor Spending ($000s)	Contribution of all Visitor Spending			
			Jobs	Labor Income ($000s)	Value Added ($000s)	Output ($000s)
Niobrara NSR	65,999	$2,621.6	37	$629.2	$1,222.2	$2,386.7
Noatak NPRES	31,000	$44,776.4	624	$22,339.5	$37,392.0	$62,295.4
North Cascades NP	26,935	$1,216.1	13	$494.7	$874.1	$1,337.5
Obed W&SR*	212,446	$3,499.4	39	$1,093.0	$1,812.6	$3,026.2
Ocmulgee NM	120,025	$6,458.7	95	$2,256.2	$4,153.2	$7,263.2
Olympic NP	2,824,908	$220,037.3	2,708	$101,925.8	$186,607.2	$288,926.6
Oregon Caves NM	78,164	$5,036.4	74	$1,871.5	$3,277.8	$5,899.4
Organ Pipe Cactus NM	161,743	$9,285.8	128	$4,669.6	$7,643.4	$12,302.6
Ozark NSR	1,406,781	$56,125.3	794	$17,574.3	$30,496.7	$56,663.6
Padre Island NS	573,855	$22,815.1	307	$7,346.8	$14,033.7	$24,278.1
Palo Alto Battlefield NHP	36,707	$1,975.2	28	$668.8	$1,316.4	$2,268.5
Pea Ridge NMP	131,907	$7,098.1	108	$2,830.9	$4,794.6	$8,509.1
Pecos NHP	45,568	$2,452.1	37	$1,054.8	$1,728.0	$2,968.4
Pennsylvania Avenue NHS	283,232	$4,929.1	65	$2,594.2	$4,254.3	$6,563.1
Perry's Victory & Intl. Peace MEM*	140,281	$11,497.2	212	$6,301.3	$10,335.7	$17,171.7
Petersburg NB	188,426	$10,139.4	147	$4,155.1	$7,168.8	$12,139.7
Petrified Forest NP	664,857	$39,405.1	488	$13,006.7	$23,088.7	$39,868.8
Petroglyph NM	119,444	$6,427.4	96	$2,728.4	$4,502.2	$7,770.7
Pictured Rocks NL	593,587	$23,721.3	312	$7,150.3	$13,090.0	$23,187.2
Pinnacles NP	224,476	$12,079.3	147	$5,455.3	$8,878.3	$14,011.9
Pipe Spring NM	54,692	$2,943.0	41	$1,061.2	$1,865.2	$3,231.6
Pipestone NM	76,030	$4,091.3	63	$1,490.0	$2,689.4	$4,886.1
Piscataway P	124,107	$6,678.3	86	$3,427.1	$5,525.7	$8,470.1
Point Reyes NS	2,412,663	$97,925.1	1,118	$48,640.0	$75,330.8	$116,592.8
Port Chicago Naval Magazine NMEM	533	$28.7	0	$15.3	$24.0	$37.5
President William Jefferson Clinton Birthplace Home NHS	8,932	$480.6	7	$177.1	$313.0	$536.1
President's Park	600,083	$10,443.3	138	$5,495.7	$9,011.5	$13,894.7
Prince William Forest P	280,325	$15,410.5	189	$7,674.2	$12,474.1	$19,193.2
Pu`uhonua O Honaunau NHP	442,353	$23,803.5	285	$11,110.8	$18,490.5	$28,568.4
Puukohola Heiau NHS	134,403	$7,232.4	86	$3,374.7	$5,615.9	$8,671.7
Rainbow Bridge NM	75,214	$4,047.4	52	$1,394.1	$2,444.6	$4,151.3
Redwood NP	352,517	$20,833.3	297	$7,498.9	$13,404.1	$23,912.2
Richmond NBP	156,952	$8,445.8	123	$3,488.0	$6,056.4	$10,182.9
Rio Grande W&SR	694	$69.1	1	$17.2	$30.7	$51.8
River Raisin NB	50,667	$2,726.5	41	$1,268.2	$2,126.3	$3,551.4
Rock Creek P	2,003,385	$34,865.2	462	$18,284.5	$30,027.1	$46,380.4
Rocky Mountain NP*	3,229,617	$196,144.0	2,779	$105,853.9	$168,376.3	$270,807.4
Roger Williams NMEM	51,944	$2,795.2	36	$1,406.5	$2,338.1	$3,600.2

Park Unit	Total Recreation Visits	Total Visitor Spending ($000s)	Contribution of all Visitor Spending			
			Jobs	Labor Income ($000s)	Value Added ($000s)	Output ($000s)
Rosie the Riveter WWII Home Front NHP	20,097	$1,081.4	13	$576.6	$901.0	$1,405.6
Ross Lake NRA	742,200	$30,357.1	336	$12,795.8	$22,445.5	$34,431.5
Russell Cave NM	20,954	$1,127.6	17	$411.8	$729.4	$1,291.3
Sagamore Hill NHS	14,639	$787.7	9	$426.7	$691.7	$1,004.7
Saguaro NP	634,286	$37,567.7	526	$19,076.0	$31,355.8	$50,551.0
Saint Croix NSR	221,028	$8,745.9	124	$3,849.7	$6,651.0	$11,129.8
Saint Croix Island IHS	0	$0.0	0	$0.0	$0.0	$0.0
Saint Paul's Church NHS	16,188	$871.1	10	$472.9	$765.2	$1,112.9
Saint-Gaudens NHS*	33,663	$1,529.6	25	$810.5	$1,353.5	$2,161.5
Salem Maritime NHS	756,038	$40,683.3	550	$21,479.3	$34,490.2	$53,809.8
Salinas Pueblo Missions NM	29,228	$1,572.8	23	$666.5	$1,097.5	$1,893.1
Salt River Bay EHP	5,217	$280.7	3	$131.0	$218.1	$336.9
San Antonio Missions NHP	614,810	$33,083.7	480	$14,131.0	$25,277.1	$41,872.0
San Francisco Maritime NHP	4,129,983	$95,335.3	1,045	$42,880.6	$66,377.1	$102,042.2
San Juan NHS	1,279,814	$68,868.3	823	$32,145.9	$53,496.6	$82,654.1
San Juan Island NHP	261,139	$14,052.2	167	$6,249.8	$11,151.2	$17,195.0
Sand Creek Massacre NHS	4,384	$235.9	3	$57.7	$115.9	$218.8
Santa Monica Mountains NRA	649,471	$26,126.7	336	$13,322.2	$21,581.7	$34,483.6
Saratoga NHP	57,688	$3,104.3	40	$1,172.0	$2,240.4	$3,588.7
Saugus Iron Works NHS	11,611	$624.8	9	$276.1	$474.4	$779.3
Scotts Bluff NM	122,515	$6,592.7	89	$2,271.2	$3,943.0	$6,913.9
Sequoia NP*	1,106,584	$77,187.1	936	$28,257.9	$50,651.0	$83,857.5
Shenandoah NP	1,210,200	$76,019.2	945	$37,528.0	$61,035.5	$94,495.8
Shiloh NMP	587,620	$31,620.5	471	$9,637.1	$18,306.4	$33,944.6
Sitka NHP	195,157	$39,879.4	955	$26,147.8	$40,611.4	$65,875.7
Sleeping Bear Dunes NL*	1,531,560	$151,782.0	2,818	$71,692.5	$126,348.4	$222,811.4
Springfield Armory NHS	16,978	$913.6	12	$436.5	$739.6	$1,146.2
Statue Of Liberty NM	3,029,443	$163,018.0	1,877	$88,700.6	$143,200.1	$209,202.2
Steamtown NHS*	106,309	$5,293.6	76	$2,380.4	$3,994.8	$6,504.2
Stones River NB	260,537	$14,019.8	204	$6,544.2	$10,789.8	$17,797.1
Sunset Crater Volcano NM	177,793	$9,567.3	122	$3,427.8	$5,806.1	$9,803.4
Tallgrass Prairie NPRES	18,918	$1,018.0	15	$389.0	$688.4	$1,197.0
Thaddeus Kosciuszko NMEM	2,045	$110.0	2	$59.4	$94.1	$150.5
Theodore Roosevelt NP	640,555	$37,439.0	470	$11,901.1	$20,593.4	$36,865.0
Theodore Roosevelt Birthplace NHS	17,930	$964.8	11	$523.9	$848.2	$1,240.4
Theodore Roosevelt Inaugural NHS	18,875	$1,015.7	13	$370.0	$757.6	$1,191.5
Theodore Roosevelt Island P	149,754	$8,058.4	105	$4,127.2	$6,667.8	$10,266.6
Thomas Edison NHP	52,554	$2,828.0	33	$1,543.9	$2,479.6	$3,638.9
Thomas Jefferson NMEM	2,613,131	$45,476.7	601	$23,930.7	$39,244.7	$60,507.2
Thomas Stone NHS	6,426	$345.8	4	$178.0	$286.2	$437.7
Timpanogos Cave NM	118,764	$6,390.8	99	$3,110.2	$5,060.6	$8,776.2

Table 5. (Continued)

Park Unit	Total Recreation Visits	Total Visitor Spending ($000s)	Contribution of all Visitor Spending			
			Jobs	Labor Income ($000s)	Value Added ($000s)	Output ($000s)
Timucuan EHP	1,076,310	$57,917.5	828	$26,237.3	$45,176.6	$73,851.3
Tonto NM	51,881	$2,791.8	40	$1,431.9	$2,326.2	$3,718.5
Tumacácori NHP	35,158	$1,891.9	26	$754.2	$1,271.6	$2,129.5
Tuskegee Airmen NHS	23,716	$1,276.2	19	$465.0	$794.7	$1,432.1
Tuskegee Institute NHS	24,030	$1,293.1	19	$471.2	$805.4	$1,451.1
Tuzigoot NM	97,388	$5,240.6	74	$2,674.2	$4,316.2	$6,868.5
Ulysses S Grant NHS	39,373	$2,118.7	33	$1,061.0	$1,741.8	$2,950.5
Upper Delaware NSR&NRR	255,586	$10,152.2	105	$4,924.5	$7,733.7	$11,259.2
Valley Forge NHP	1,442,750	$77,598.6	1,101	$41,827.5	$66,384.6	$106,382.0
Vanderbilt Mansion NHS	423,107	$22,767.9	274	$11,021.2	$18,612.3	$27,860.0
Vicksburg NMP	573,262	$30,847.9	454	$12,576.0	$21,315.6	$37,233.9
Vietnam Veterans MEM	4,424,407	$76,998.6	1,017	$40,518.0	$66,446.9	$102,447.4
Virgin Islands NP*	483,341	$69,936.8	875	$37,046.7	$64,945.3	$100,042.9
Voyageurs NP	214,841	$16,158.9	225	$5,081.2	$10,362.4	$17,846.3
Walnut Canyon NM	110,748	$5,959.5	76	$2,135.2	$3,616.6	$6,106.6
War In The Pacific NHP	255,923	$13,771.5	176	$6,958.8	$11,288.0	$17,443.4
Washington Monument	0	$0.0	0	$0.0	$0.0	$0.0
Washita Battlefield NHS	10,615	$571.2	8	$178.8	$320.7	$578.4
Weir Farm NHS	21,465	$1,155.1	13	$621.0	$1,011.2	$1,471.3
Whiskeytown NRA	814,374	$32,530.3	419	$10,582.8	$19,714.7	$33,954.1
White House	656,949	$11,433.0	151	$6,016.2	$9,866.2	$15,211.7
White Sands NM*	447,385	$21,857.2	276	$6,978.4	$13,023.9	$22,704.6
Whitman Mission NHS	60,785	$3,270.9	42	$1,014.1	$2,037.6	$3,442.3
William Howard Taft NHS	19,416	$1,044.8	16	$467.3	$793.2	$1,358.1
Wilson's Creek NB	167,205	$8,997.5	138	$3,640.4	$6,086.2	$10,813.3
Wind Cave NP*	529,083	$48,978.5	789	$18,274.7	$33,065.6	$59,350.7
Wolf Trap NP for the Performing Arts	426,996	$22,977.2	299	$11,747.7	$18,998.7	$29,313.1
Women's Rights NHP*	29,585	$1,973.2	23	$641.5	$1,461.8	$2,302.5
World War II Memorial	4,161,685	$72,426.4	957	$38,112.1	$62,501.3	$96,364.1
World War II Valor in the Pacific NM	1,751,224	$94,235.5	1,126	$43,986.5	$73,201.6	$113,099.1
Wrangell - St Elias NP&PRES	87,158	$125,890.9	1,754	$62,891.0	$105,606.3	$175,299.6
Wright Brothers NMEM	466,816	$25,119.9	364	$9,893.1	$17,009.1	$28,933.6
Wupatki NM	201,365	$10,835.7	139	$3,932.5	$6,639.5	$11,191.5
Yellowstone NP*	3,447,729	$400,346.5	5,619	$164,989.6	$271,976.6	$472,960.9
Yosemite NP*	3,853,404	$378,757.7	5,162	$161,602.1	$284,264.6	$471,805.8

Park Unit	Total Recreation Visits	Total Visitor Spending ($000s)	Contribution of all Visitor Spending			
			Jobs	Labor Income ($000s)	Value Added ($000s)	Output ($000s)
Yukon - Charley Rivers NPRES	1,393	$1,603.5	18	$813.7	$1,453.8	$2,335.5
Zion NP*	2,973,607	$152,859.4	1,854	$76,269.3	$124,961.5	$192,796.6

*For these parks, results are based on a visitor survey at the designated park. For other parks, visitor characteristics and spending averages are adapted from national averages for each park type.

Table 6. Visits, spending and economic impacts to local economies of NPS visitors spending

Park Unit	Non-Local Recreation Visits	Non-Local Visitor Spending ($000s)	Impact of Non-Local Visitor Spending			
			Jobs	Labor Income ($000s)	Value Added ($000s)	Output ($000s)
Abraham Lincoln Birthplace NHP	142,393	$8,713.8	131	$3,776.6	$6,521.0	$11,104.3
Acadia NP	2,303,345	$197,967.1	3,051	$91,209.3	$150,622.4	$261,017.7
Adams NHP	282,266	$17,273.4	233	$9,053.4	$14,737.5	$23,012.2
African Burial Ground NM	65,204	$3,990.2	46	$2,178.6	$3,533.5	$5,167.2
Agate Fossil Beds NM*	11,305	$792.8	10	$215.2	$403.4	$768.3
Alibates Flint Quarries NM	2,842	$173.9	3	$57.1	$113.2	$198.5
Allegheny Portage Railroad NHS	116,646	$7,138.2	108	$3,203.3	$5,301.2	$9,068.5
Amistad NRA	932,619	$48,520.5	617	$13,330.0	$26,805.6	$47,086.0
Andersonville NHS	103,222	$6,316.7	95	$2,152.6	$3,997.6	$7,199.4
Andrew Johnson NHS	43,059	$2,635.0	39	$1,073.8	$1,871.5	$3,197.8
Aniakchak NM&PRES	18	$28.9	0	$14.4	$24.3	$40.3
Antietam NB	429,173	$26,263.5	345	$13,449.1	$21,788.0	$33,799.5
Apostle Islands NL*	151,365	$23,674.4	325	$7,584.7	$14,827.8	$25,693.2
Appomattox Court House NHP	269,361	$16,483.7	238	$6,128.2	$10,937.4	$18,950.7
Arches NP*	1,070,577	$115,859.9	1,708	$44,827.1	$79,851.3	$138,019.2
Arkansas Post NMEM	37,169	$2,322.3	31	$967.0	$1,581.8	$2,677.2
Arlington House, The Robert E. Lee Memorial NMEM	472,728	$28,928.9	375	$14,893.6	$24,121.0	$37,166.6
Assateague Island NS	1,481,398	$76,319.0	974	$26,809.7	$48,940.6	$81,576.8
Aztec Ruins NM	37,586	$2,300.0	31	$765.9	$1,339.3	$2,376.3
Badlands NP	828,876	$51,475.1	771	$17,989.9	$32,577.0	$59,641.6
Bandelier NM	141,141	$8,599.3	123	$3,607.4	$5,975.9	$10,338.8
Bent's Old Fort NHS	21,685	$1,327.0	18	$508.8	$886.3	$1,498.7
Bering Land Bridge NPRES	2,642	$3,816.1	53	$1,906.4	$3,201.2	$5,313.8
Big Bend NP	280,028	$23,952.1	318	$6,971.1	$14,345.7	$24,858.9
Big Cypress NPRES	831,009	$63,595.3	846	$33,472.3	$55,609.8	$87,630.0

Table 6. (Continued)

Park Unit	Non-Local Recreation Visits	Non-Local Visitor Spending ($000s)	Impact of Non-Local Visitor Spending			
			Jobs	Labor Income ($000s)	Value Added ($000s)	Output ($000s)
Big Hole NB	29,574	$1,809.8	27	$653.6	$1,054.8	$1,953.6
Big South Fork NRRA*	343,362	$13,727.4	180	$4,796.8	$8,546.9	$14,570.6
Big Thicket NPRES	126,753	$7,858.1	98	$3,472.6	$5,929.5	$9,475.5
Bighorn Canyon NRA	169,953	$8,695.5	127	$3,282.6	$5,452.5	$9,826.8
Biscayne NP	464,395	$28,809.8	372	$14,971.9	$24,443.8	$38,216.3
Black Canyon Of The Gunnison NP	181,153	$10,887.3	132	$4,579.6	$7,379.8	$11,897.6
Blue Ridge PKWY	14,240,414	$890,614.1	12,026	$421,159.6	$718,233.9	$1,147,391.4
Bluestone NSR	25,791	$1,299.5	17	$467.7	$790.9	$1,361.0
Booker T Washington NM	20,463	$1,252.3	18	$487.4	$846.7	$1,461.9
Boston NHP	2,208,414	$135,145.1	1,827	$71,083.0	$115,473.3	$180,444.4
Boston African American NHS	339,568	$20,780.1	281	$10,921.4	$17,749.7	$27,744.4
Brown V Board Of Education NHS	17,724	$1,084.7	17	$540.6	$882.1	$1,496.1
Bryce Canyon NP	1,309,663	$107,196.1	1,480	$39,808.9	$71,616.2	$123,522.6
Buck Island Reef NM	28,667	$1,705.3	19	$770.4	$1,306.9	$2,011.4
Buffalo NR	756,117	$38,791.0	550	$13,889.8	$24,003.5	$42,965.6
Cabrillo NM	737,479	$45,130.4	571	$21,500.0	$34,899.9	$54,512.8
Canaveral NS	931,079	$58,112.9	776	$26,484.1	$45,784.7	$73,566.3
Cane River Creole NHP	23,781	$1,455.3	20	$530.9	$971.8	$1,677.5
Canyon De Chelly NM	777,139	$49,920.8	660	$15,696.8	$28,358.0	$51,372.1
Canyonlands NP	427,747	$24,899.1	335	$8,941.5	$15,874.3	$27,512.6
Cape Cod NS	3,027,104	$158,074.5	1,937	$79,823.2	$126,079.2	$194,000.2
Cape Hatteras NS	2,158,267	$133,288.1	1,863	$51,606.3	$89,882.2	$153,063.0
Cape Krusenstern NM	24,950	$36,037.8	502	$18,003.3	$30,231.0	$50,181.6
Cape Lookout NS	332,007	$18,684.2	270	$6,106.2	$10,925.9	$19,731.7
Capitol Reef NP*	659,478	$44,453.8	553	$15,043.6	$26,862.5	$47,252.4
Capulin Volcano NM*	46,933	$1,333.3	18	$346.8	$649.4	$1,196.2
Carl Sandburg Home NHS	78,481	$4,802.6	70	$1,926.0	$3,318.7	$5,706.3
Carlsbad Caverns NP	356,741	$22,285.8	293	$7,176.1	$12,460.7	$22,517.4
Casa Grande Ruins NM	57,650	$3,527.9	51	$1,832.1	$2,982.3	$4,804.7
Castillo De San Marcos NM	610,885	$37,383.4	533	$16,294.4	$28,759.7	$47,167.5
Castle Clinton NM	1,326,852	$46,628.1	516	$23,453.2	$37,458.9	$54,679.6
Catoctin Mountain P	248,188	$14,900.9	189	$7,469.6	$12,161.7	$18,916.2
Cedar Breaks NM	591,562	$36,920.7	494	$13,048.2	$23,374.7	$40,632.8
Chaco Culture NHP	36,687	$2,226.3	32	$883.5	$1,494.3	$2,611.2
Chamizal NMEM	87,484	$5,353.7	76	$1,934.0	$3,606.1	$6,275.2
Channel Islands NP	235,465	$13,823.4	176	$7,259.9	$11,743.9	$18,560.2
Charles Pinckney NHS	37,224	$2,277.9	33	$974.7	$1,618.1	$2,695.7
Chattahoochee River NRA	2,217,696	$111,743.0	1,605	$56,651.6	$91,832.4	$150,126.7

Park Unit	Non-Local Recreation Visits	Non-Local Visitor Spending ($000s)	Impact of Non-Local Visitor Spending			
			Jobs	Labor Income ($000s)	Value Added ($000s)	Output ($000s)
Chesapeake & Ohio Canal NHP	3,928,807	$74,952.4	1,022	$38,732.3	$64,567.3	$101,708.1
Chickamauga & Chattanooga NMP	967,045	$60,357.7	857	$21,202.9	$38,720.2	$68,708.1
Chickasaw NRA*	882,483	$13,487.2	153	$3,524.8	$6,144.3	$11,124.5
Chiricahua NM	38,798	$2,293.0	29	$688.1	$1,269.4	$2,244.8
Christiansted NHS	106,649	$6,526.4	78	$3,062.3	$5,108.2	$7,896.8
City Of Rocks NRES	83,156	$5,088.8	70	$1,859.9	$3,116.9	$5,472.4
Clara Barton NHS	21,292	$1,302.9	17	$670.5	$1,086.0	$1,675.1
Colonial NHP	2,750,317	$168,307.2	2,427	$71,202.0	$122,280.2	$206,032.6
Colorado NM	426,322	$26,230.9	352	$9,530.5	$16,925.9	$29,056.4
Congaree NP*	77,026	$4,850.4	63	$1,799.7	$3,117.7	$5,364.0
Coronado NMEM	81,967	$5,016.0	69	$2,006.5	$3,392.0	$5,696.0
Cowpens NB	217,167	$13,568.4	199	$6,259.3	$10,497.0	$17,733.9
Crater Lake NP	424,159	$35,563.1	544	$15,384.7	$25,386.6	$44,529.9
Craters Of The Moon NM&PRES*	187,690	$6,249.4	90	$2,002.0	$3,481.2	$6,561.5
Cumberland Gap NHP	800,056	$49,707.2	694	$19,279.4	$34,645.1	$59,383.3
Cumberland Island NS	45,028	$2,145.8	29	$924.6	$1,552.7	$2,547.7
Curecanti NRA	596,499	$30,510.7	373	$12,088.4	$19,636.1	$32,148.5
Cuyahoga Valley NP	2,153,214	$134,950.9	2,032	$58,471.2	$100,744.8	$173,714.7
Dayton Aviation Heritage NHP*	40,542	$3,315.1	55	$1,676.9	$2,821.2	$4,825.0
De Soto NMEM	363,704	$22,257.1	318	$10,874.1	$18,591.5	$29,986.8
Death Valley NP	933,367	$76,782.7	916	$35,237.5	$58,622.5	$90,253.0
Delaware Water Gap NRA*	3,419,219	$131,519.7	1,928	$82,474.8	$126,488.0	$182,946.3
Denali NP&PRES	388,433	$371,501.1	5,098	$185,911.3	$313,678.5	$520,780.6
Devils Postpile NM	82,417	$5,061.1	65	$1,891.7	$3,410.7	$5,705.2
Devils Tower NM	390,829	$24,196.1	348	$8,494.2	$15,206.1	$27,461.7
Dinosaur NM	285,821	$16,727.5	199	$6,084.4	$10,148.0	$16,969.2
Dry Tortugas NP	57,540	$3,173.6	33	$1,229.6	$2,050.2	$3,196.0
Edgar Allan Poe NHS	16,048	$982.0	14	$533.4	$846.5	$1,354.9
Effigy Mounds NM*	68,890	$4,409.3	65	$1,598.5	$2,774.1	$4,972.2
Eisenhower NHS	44,760	$2,739.1	36	$1,399.5	$2,256.0	$3,510.6
El Malpais NM	107,359	$6,707.4	97	$2,700.2	$4,597.1	$8,061.5
El Morro NM	42,053	$2,575.4	35	$640.9	$1,283.7	$2,444.2
Eleanor Roosevelt NHS	46,241	$2,829.8	34	$1,351.7	$2,314.3	$3,474.0
Eugene O'Neill NHS	2,343	$143.4	2	$76.9	$120.3	$187.9
Everglades NP	1,019,068	$99,924.3	1,368	$55,426.8	$91,952.0	$143,932.7
Federal Hall NMEM	140,402	$8,592.0	99	$4,704.4	$7,606.1	$11,111.8
Fire Island NS	336,075	$17,074.0	185	$8,924.7	$14,359.1	$20,890.5
First Ladies NHS	8,318	$509.1	8	$241.3	$400.3	$679.5
Flight 93 NMEM	267,058	$16,342.8	247	$7,327.1	$12,164.4	$20,775.6
Florissant Fossil Beds NM	52,615	$3,219.8	45	$1,711.8	$2,703.0	$4,332.6
Ford's Theatre NHS	584,465	$11,173.0	147	$5,953.3	$9,819.7	$15,162.0

Table 6. (Continued)

Park Unit	Non-Local Recreation Visits	Non-Local Visitor Spending ($000s)	Impact of Non-Local Visitor Spending			
			Jobs	Labor Income ($000s)	Value Added ($000s)	Output ($000s)
Fort Bowie NHS	6,692	$409.5	6	$161.5	$272.9	$459.2
Fort Caroline NMEM	274,965	$16,826.6	241	$7,699.0	$13,287.5	$21,734.1
Fort Davis NHS	32,034	$1,960.4	26	$537.9	$1,104.9	$1,939.7
Fort Donelson NB	266,588	$16,654.7	224	$7,516.4	$12,459.6	$20,344.6
Fort Frederica NM	220,278	$13,480.0	188	$5,977.7	$10,095.2	$16,584.5
Fort Laramie NHS	46,368	$2,837.5	39	$962.1	$1,732.4	$3,059.9
Fort Larned NHS*	29,646	$1,812.9	24	$531.2	$1,019.6	$1,895.4
Fort Matanzas NM	417,963	$25,577.4	361	$11,126.5	$19,605.0	$31,997.5
Fort McHenry NM&SHRINE	625,024	$38,248.7	502	$19,656.8	$32,093.8	$49,753.5
Fort Necessity NB	175,925	$10,979.2	161	$4,998.4	$8,325.5	$14,121.2
Fort Point NHS	1,262,339	$77,249.6	956	$41,452.6	$64,844.6	$101,327.4
Fort Pulaski NM	361,130	$22,562.8	303	$9,208.8	$15,602.3	$25,961.1
Fort Raleigh NHS	236,739	$14,487.4	211	$5,730.5	$9,892.0	$16,888.6
Fort Scott NHS*	14,857	$310.1	4	$82.8	$149.1	$280.6
Fort Smith NHS	73,403	$4,492.0	67	$1,602.6	$2,846.5	$5,164.2
Fort Stanwix NM*	136,539	$9,539.4	113	$3,108.6	$6,909.5	$10,962.4
Fort Sumter NM	707,303	$43,283.6	621	$18,489.0	$30,758.9	$51,287.9
Fort Union NM*	8,930	$571.4	7	$213.5	$342.3	$583.1
Fort Union Trading Post NHS*	11,132	$909.5	10	$273.9	$443.8	$760.8
Fort Vancouver NHS	572,380	$35,027.1	535	$17,100.8	$27,849.5	$47,561.8
Fort Washington P	309,812	$18,959.1	243	$9,778.4	$15,804.1	$24,228.0
Fossil Butte NM*	17,084	$786.9	9	$258.6	$436.4	$740.5
Franklin Delano Roosevelt MEM	2,303,113	$44,027.8	581	$23,459.2	$38,694.8	$59,746.5
Frederick Douglass NHS	44,416	$849.1	11	$453.1	$746.5	$1,150.9
Frederick Law Olmsted NHS	7,281	$445.6	6	$233.4	$380.6	$594.9
Fredericksburg & Spotsylvania NMP	825,152	$50,495.6	642	$25,436.0	$40,872.0	$63,083.6
Friendship Hill NHS	28,803	$1,762.6	27	$811.0	$1,337.7	$2,263.7
Gates Of The Arctic NP&PRES	10,899	$15,742.5	219	$7,864.4	$13,205.9	$21,921.0
Gateway NRA	2,047,112	$71,955.2	812	$36,608.4	$58,136.4	$85,527.3
Gauley River NRA	79,390	$4,081.4	54	$1,504.4	$2,483.4	$4,288.3
General Grant NMEM	77,631	$4,750.7	55	$2,593.6	$4,209.2	$6,157.7
George Rogers Clark NHP	105,816	$6,475.5	95	$2,225.9	$4,118.4	$7,341.0
George Washington MEM PKWY	1,039,581	$6,303.9	105	$3,468.6	$5,272.4	$8,204.5
George Washington Birthplace NM*	116,346	$5,392.8	66	$2,676.3	$4,272.4	$6,572.4
George Washington Carver NM*	23,140	$493.1	6	$168.0	$282.5	$499.4
Park Unit	Non-Local	Non-Local	Impact of Non-Local Visitor Spending			

	Recreation Visits	Visitor Spending ($000s)	Jobs	Labor Income ($000s)	Value Added ($000s)	Output ($000s)
Gettysburg NMP	1,055,710	$65,446.4	829	$32,678.4	$53,279.5	$83,098.3
Gila Cliff Dwellings NM	24,055	$1,472.1	21	$383.7	$745.5	$1,404.2
Glacier NP	2,048,564	$169,797.2	2,717	$73,200.8	$118,519.1	$215,588.0
Glacier Bay NP&PRES	454,337	$92,676.3	1,661	$49,742.6	$77,034.6	$121,675.5
Glen Canyon NRA	2,061,328	$114,888.1	1,436	$39,140.3	$68,381.6	$117,506.6
Golden Gate NRA*	5,905,577	$209,761.8	2,466	$103,242.7	$161,065.2	$250,134.8
Golden Spike NHS	38,851	$2,197.0	31	$963.8	$1,592.7	$2,780.4
Governors Island NM	292,529	$17,901.5	206	$9,801.6	$15,847.4	$23,151.5
Grand Canyon NP*	4,421,352	$453,641.3	6,010	$225,593.2	$381,343.5	$574,714.9
Grand Portage NM	87,219	$5,445.0	71	$1,396.6	$2,879.0	$5,181.3
Grand Teton NP	2,509,217	$449,530.8	6,286	$186,459.6	$305,211.3	$535,718.3
Grant-Kohrs Ranch NHS	14,360	$878.8	14	$388.3	$605.8	$1,098.7
Great Basin NP	90,399	$4,857.9	59	$1,382.3	$2,566.9	$4,527.7
Great Sand Dunes NP&PRES	240,165	$14,144.6	186	$5,249.6	$9,204.3	$15,677.3
Great Smoky Mountains NP	9,135,241	$728,768.3	10,791	$317,185.1	$553,409.5	$938,810.3
Greenbelt P	136,881	$8,247.0	102	$4,131.1	$6,749.6	$10,383.9
Guadalupe Mountains NP	149,944	$8,995.8	119	$3,115.6	$5,803.3	$9,998.9
Guilford Courthouse NMP	293,372	$18,329.5	269	$8,170.1	$13,681.3	$23,283.4
Gulf Islands NS	3,412,264	$176,225.6	2,398	$73,805.5	$124,308.6	$206,537.3
Hagerman Fossil Beds NM	20,106	$1,230.4	18	$540.0	$861.4	$1,487.1
Haleakala NP	1,025,759	$63,614.2	728	$29,041.3	$49,295.0	$75,883.5
Hamilton Grange NMEM	13,740	$840.9	10	$458.5	$744.2	$1,086.9
Hampton NHS	31,525	$1,929.2	25	$998.9	$1,624.7	$2,523.3
Harpers Ferry NHP*	210,485	$10,994.7	155	$6,092.3	$9,798.1	$15,147.6
Harry S Truman NHS	26,305	$1,609.8	25	$816.7	$1,324.4	$2,253.4
Hawaii Volcanoes NP	1,400,587	$111,449.3	1,331	$52,501.2	$90,498.2	$138,624.2
Herbert Hoover NHS	108,203	$6,621.5	99	$2,554.1	$4,526.8	$8,000.5
Home Of Franklin D Roosevelt NHS	114,026	$6,977.9	84	$3,397.5	$5,755.8	$8,627.3
Homestead NM*	78,914	$2,950.7	40	$928.3	$1,642.7	$3,025.0
Hopewell Culture NHP	33,148	$2,028.5	31	$941.5	$1,575.0	$2,681.6
Hopewell Furnace NHS	44,411	$2,717.7	39	$1,420.0	$2,295.3	$3,747.6
Horseshoe Bend NMP	49,281	$3,015.8	45	$1,306.0	$2,151.4	$3,749.6
Hot Springs NP	1,219,810	$75,994.7	1,095	$30,982.0	$53,532.9	$93,732.7
Hovenweep NM	25,070	$1,534.3	20	$533.2	$931.6	$1,618.0
Hubbell Trading Post NHS	63,051	$3,858.5	53	$1,221.8	$2,178.8	$3,947.8
Independence NHP	3,019,421	$184,775.2	2,601	$100,368.8	$159,271.7	$254,934.5
Indiana Dunes NL	1,289,857	$67,021.9	848	$33,557.6	$56,999.7	$88,678.4
Isle Royale NP	16,664	$3,477.1	50	$1,155.8	$2,185.9	$3,777.4
James A Garfield NHS*	24,810	$1,092.6	18	$499.4	$849.2	$1,478.2
Jean Lafitte NP&PRES	352,544	$21,574.1	302	$9,460.4	$15,940.2	$26,541.0
Jefferson NEM*	2,296,988	$225,997.2	3,845	$120,057.1	$198,834.5	$334,754.0
Jewel Cave NM	91,812	$5,618.5	85	$1,988.7	$3,569.2	$6,474.7
Jimmy Carter NHS	58,749	$3,595.2	54	$1,223.4	$2,266.1	$4,080.8

Table 6. (Continued)

Park Unit	Non-Local Recreation Visits	Non-Local Visitor Spending ($000s)	Impact of Non-Local Visitor Spending			
			Jobs	Labor Income ($000s)	Value Added ($000s)	Output ($000s)
John D Rockefeller Jr MEM PKWY	1,103,403	$37,449.2	579	$18,509.2	$30,645.5	$57,637.2
John Day Fossil Beds NM*	139,550	$6,404.2	87	$2,309.2	$3,845.0	$7,042.9
John F Kennedy NHS	19,020	$1,163.9	16	$609.1	$993.8	$1,553.9
John Muir NHS	31,418	$1,922.7	24	$1,031.1	$1,614.2	$2,523.9
Johnstown Flood NMEM*	94,937	$6,390.4	106	$3,068.4	$5,083.8	$8,736.3
Joshua Tree NP*	1,282,421	$61,599.1	767	$29,105.9	$48,285.8	$76,237.0
Kalaupapa NHP	49,456	$3,026.4	36	$1,420.1	$2,368.8	$3,661.9
Kaloko-Honokohau NHP	129,011	$7,894.9	94	$3,704.4	$6,179.3	$9,552.6
Katmai NP&PRES	39,818	$57,513.1	801	$28,731.7	$48,246.1	$80,085.3
Kenai Fjords NP	281,279	$52,487.9	965	$28,359.6	$43,509.5	$68,349.9
Kennesaw Mountain NBP	1,626,164	$99,514.0	1,488	$52,825.2	$86,075.9	$140,335.8
Kings Canyon NP	562,231	$45,238.3	597	$18,001.9	$32,041.3	$53,273.3
Kings Mountain NMP*	161,992	$8,804.9	130	$4,102.3	$6,869.2	$11,663.2
Klondike Gold Rush NHP	854,249	$160,289.5	2,942	$86,568.5	$132,894.4	$208,840.2
Klondike Gold Rush NHP	50,566	$3,094.4	38	$1,385.0	$2,508.4	$3,902.1
Knife River Indian Villages NHS	13,448	$823.0	12	$304.3	$542.7	$952.5
Kobuk Valley NP	29,550	$42,682.0	595	$21,322.5	$35,804.7	$59,433.5
Korean War Veterans MEM	2,721,891	$52,033.4	687	$27,724.8	$45,730.7	$70,610.2
Lake Chelan NRA	29,111	$1,712.6	20	$757.4	$1,344.2	$2,069.0
Lake Clark NP&PRES	11,639	$16,811.4	234	$8,398.4	$14,102.6	$23,409.3
Lake Mead NRA	4,392,290	$224,126.2	2,571	$95,591.1	$154,513.9	$238,772.0
Lake Meredith NRA	345,610	$17,793.4	247	$5,683.5	$11,021.3	$19,433.8
Lake Roosevelt NRA	1,238,476	$63,527.4	811	$22,340.2	$43,510.5	$71,586.1
Lassen Volcanic NP	385,430	$22,644.9	294	$7,378.7	$14,115.3	$24,488.6
Lava Beds NM*	152,808	$6,814.0	83	$2,227.0	$3,855.5	$6,711.8
Lewis and Clark NHP	169,432	$10,368.4	146	$4,661.1	$7,807.1	$13,040.4
Lincoln MEM	5,158,117	$98,605.9	1,301	$52,539.8	$86,662.0	$133,809.9
Lincoln Boyhood NMEM*	113,230	$5,751.6	92	$2,611.1	$4,414.6	$7,498.0
Lincoln Home NHS*	265,930	$16,156.8	210	$5,304.5	$11,194.0	$18,515.5
Little Bighorn Battlefield NM	290,916	$17,802.7	276	$7,212.7	$11,685.5	$21,194.6
Little River Canyon NPRES	168,932	$10,337.9	153	$4,056.7	$7,104.4	$12,314.8
Little Rock Central High School NHS	53,708	$3,286.7	50	$1,388.1	$2,373.9	$4,163.2
Longfellow NHS	43,876	$2,685.1	36	$1,410.7	$2,294.3	$3,588.0
Lowell NHP	451,543	$27,632.4	378	$14,496.2	$23,547.9	$36,979.3
Lyndon B Johnson NHP	93,064	$5,695.1	80	$2,576.9	$4,498.4	$7,335.6
Lyndon Baines Johnson Memorial Grove on the Potomac NMEM	311,693	$19,074.2	247	$9,820.0	$15,904.2	$24,505.8
Maggie L Walker NHS	6,952	$425.4	6	$176.1	$305.4	$513.8

Park Unit	Non-Local Recreation Visits	Non-Local Visitor Spending ($000s)	Impact of Non-Local Visitor Spending			
			Jobs	Labor Income ($000s)	Value Added ($000s)	Output ($000s)
Mammoth Cave NP	481,281	$39,810.5	566	$18,903.7	$31,307.5	$51,338.4
Manassas NBP	504,297	$30,860.8	397	$15,887.3	$25,688.0	$39,508.1
Manzanar NHS*	71,248	$6,937.4	86	$2,517.7	$4,517.0	$7,583.6
Marsh - Billings - Rockefeller NHP	27,218	$1,665.7	23	$689.0	$1,212.8	$1,981.1
Martin Luther King Jr NHS	594,312	$36,369.2	544	$19,492.3	$31,695.0	$51,570.1
Martin Luther King, Jr. MEM	3,114,465	$59,538.1	786	$31,723.5	$52,326.4	$80,794.2
Martin Van Buren NHS	18,532	$1,134.1	14	$489.4	$894.0	$1,373.5
Mary McLeod Bethune Council House NHS	5,537	$105.8	1	$56.4	$93.0	$143.6
Mesa Verde NP*	478,948	$46,576.0	644	$16,982.6	$29,793.1	$51,488.9
Minute Man NHP	841,014	$51,466.3	700	$27,045.6	$44,007.7	$68,966.0
Minuteman Missile NHS*	75,654	$5,173.3	77	$1,773.3	$3,281.8	$6,058.0
Mississippi NRRA	74,713	$3,764.6	54	$1,722.2	$2,984.7	$4,987.9
Missouri NRR	117,444	$5,917.6	88	$2,058.3	$3,645.6	$6,735.9
Mojave NPRES	455,871	$27,872.4	339	$12,686.9	$20,758.5	$32,129.6
Monocacy NB*	31,133	$3,387.9	44	$1,776.0	$2,922.5	$4,536.7
Montezuma Castle NM	382,456	$23,404.6	332	$11,976.5	$19,388.5	$30,947.3
Moores Creek NB	74,325	$4,621.7	64	$1,628.0	$2,972.0	$5,133.1
Morristown NHP	247,469	$15,144.0	180	$8,378.5	$13,478.2	$19,934.4
Mount Rainier NP*	964,724	$35,546.7	416	$15,301.7	$27,604.1	$42,693.5
Mount Rushmore NMEM	1,835,776	$112,341.3	1,734	$40,755.3	$73,010.6	$132,365.6
Muir Woods NM	816,758	$49,982.0	613	$26,734.2	$41,714.1	$64,879.7
Natchez NHP	155,023	$9,486.7	132	$3,697.6	$6,332.1	$10,924.5
Natchez Trace PKWY	1,231,497	$50,342.4	657	$18,031.7	$30,234.7	$50,251.9
National Capital Parks Central	715,396	$13,676.0	181	$7,281.5	$12,017.7	$18,575.1
National Capital Parks East	769,010	$14,700.9	198	$7,789.8	$12,988.9	$20,239.7
National Park of American Samoa	8,769	$536.7	6	$251.8	$420.0	$649.3
Natural Bridges NM	83,636	$5,074.5	63	$1,702.7	$3,012.7	$5,168.8
Navajo NM	54,622	$3,353.8	41	$1,129.9	$1,995.8	$3,419.9
New Bedford Whaling NHP*	235,426	$12,672.9	183	$6,920.1	$11,231.2	$17,225.4
New Orleans Jazz NHP	149,444	$9,145.3	129	$4,189.8	$6,941.2	$11,439.0
New River Gorge NR	769,705	$40,026.2	542	$14,595.1	$24,741.6	$42,812.9
Nez Perce NHP	195,798	$11,982.0	168	$4,250.3	$8,236.8	$13,982.7
Nicodemus NHS*	3,331	$177.7	2	$44.1	$86.2	$153.8
Ninety Six NHS	61,358	$3,754.8	56	$1,473.0	$2,589.4	$4,502.6
Niobrara NSR	46,200	$2,327.8	33	$567.0	$1,116.4	$2,190.8
Noatak NPRES	31,000	$44,776.4	624	$22,339.5	$37,392.0	$62,295.4
North Cascades NP	26,075	$1,205.6	13	$491.2	$868.3	$1,329.1
Obed W&SR*	113,969	$2,625.8	30	$856.2	$1,433.3	$2,397.8
Ocmulgee NM	100,821	$6,169.8	90	$2,161.6	$3,991.8	$6,999.0
Olympic NP	2,669,954	$216,454.4	2,668	$100,470.6	$184,074.4	$285,153.6
Oregon Caves NM	73,416	$4,975.0	73	$1,853.1	$3,249.0	$5,852.5
Organ Pipe Cactus NM	152,100	$9,167.3	127	$4,626.2	$7,575.1	$12,198.6

Table 6. (Continued)

Park Unit	Non-Local Recreation Visits	Non-Local Visitor Spending ($000s)	Impact of Non-Local Visitor Spending			
			Jobs	Labor Income ($000s)	Value Added ($000s)	Output ($000s)
Ozark NSR	987,582	$49,906.7	718	$15,893.2	$27,788.8	$51,992.2
Padre Island NS	400,909	$20,249.6	277	$6,636.9	$12,791.8	$22,231.0
Palo Alto Battlefield NHP	30,834	$1,886.9	27	$637.9	$1,263.4	$2,184.6
Pea Ridge NMP	110,802	$6,780.6	103	$2,716.2	$4,608.6	$8,201.1
Pecos NHP	38,277	$2,342.4	35	$1,012.5	$1,660.9	$2,860.3
Pennsylvania Avenue NHS	235,965	$4,510.9	60	$2,403.9	$3,965.0	$6,125.7
Perry's Victory & Intl. Peace MEM*	109,903	$10,287.7	187	$5,648.4	$9,274.3	$15,462.8
Petersburg NB	158,277	$9,685.9	140	$3,984.4	$6,893.4	$11,699.4
Petrified Forest NP	622,432	$38,883.6	483	$12,861.7	$22,861.8	$39,520.2
Petroglyph NM	100,334	$6,139.9	92	$2,618.6	$4,327.2	$7,487.7
Pictured Rocks NL	410,103	$20,999.5	280	$6,467.1	$11,922.9	$21,204.7
Pinnacles NP	188,560	$11,539.0	141	$5,237.4	$8,539.8	$13,507.5
Pipe Spring NM	45,942	$2,811.4	39	$1,015.9	$1,791.3	$3,114.2
Pipestone NM	63,866	$3,908.3	60	$1,428.9	$2,585.6	$4,708.3
Piscataway P	104,250	$6,379.6	82	$3,290.7	$5,319.2	$8,159.1
Point Reyes NS	1,650,677	$86,621.5	1,009	$44,340.8	$68,790.6	$106,806.4
Port Chicago Naval Magazine NMEM	447	$27.4	0	$14.7	$23.1	$36.2
President William Jefferson Clinton Birthplace Home NHS	7,503	$459.1	6	$169.5	$300.7	$516.4
President's Park	499,938	$9,557.1	126	$5,092.5	$8,398.9	$12,969.0
Prince William Forest P	265,157	$15,224.1	187	$7,604.6	$12,368.6	$19,035.6
Pu`uhonua O Honaunau NHP	371,576	$22,738.8	271	$10,669.5	$17,797.5	$27,513.4
Puukohola Heiau NHS	112,898	$6,908.9	82	$3,240.7	$5,405.4	$8,351.5
Rainbow Bridge NM	63,181	$3,866.3	50	$1,332.9	$2,346.8	$4,000.2
Redwood NP	330,158	$20,558.4	294	$7,419.3	$13,276.6	$23,706.2
Richmond NBP	131,840	$8,068.0	118	$3,344.3	$5,823.5	$9,812.6
Rio Grande W&SR	1,168	$69.1	1	$17.2	$30.7	$51.8
River Raisin NB	42,561	$2,604.5	39	$1,219.9	$2,047.0	$3,423.8
Rock Creek P	1,669,050	$31,906.7	422	$16,941.6	$27,984.2	$43,289.6
Rocky Mountain NP*	2,950,262	$189,981.9	2,696	$103,085.5	$164,151.0	$264,266.7
Roger Williams NMEM	43,634	$2,670.1	34	$1,348.3	$2,249.6	$3,466.5
Rosie the Riveter WWII Home Front NHP	16,882	$1,033.1	13	$554.4	$867.2	$1,355.1
Ross Lake NRA	518,722	$27,041.9	304	$11,653.6	$20,572.2	$31,639.7
Russell Cave NM	17,601	$1,077.1	16	$394.3	$700.6	$1,244.4
Sagamore Hill NHS	12,297	$752.5	8	$409.9	$666.0	$967.6
Saguaro NP	593,868	$37,070.9	520	$18,893.6	$31,068.0	$50,112.5
Saint Croix NSR	155,987	$7,781.1	112	$3,505.1	$6,083.9	$10,208.5
Saint Croix Island IHS	0	$0.0	0	$0.0	$0.0	$0.0
Saint Paul's Church NHS	13,597	$832.1	9	$454.2	$736.7	$1,071.8

Park Unit	Non-Local Recreation Visits	Non-Local Visitor Spending ($000s)	Impact of Non-Local Visitor Spending			
			Jobs	Labor Income ($000s)	Value Added ($000s)	Output ($000s)
Saint-Gaudens NHS*	27,167	$1,402.8	23	$745.7	$1,256.9	$2,009.5
Salem Maritime NHS	635,071	$38,863.6	524	$20,596.2	$33,187.0	$51,806.0
Salinas Pueblo Missions NM	24,552	$1,502.4	22	$639.6	$1,054.7	$1,824.2
Salt River Bay EHP	4,382	$268.2	3	$125.8	$209.9	$324.5
San Antonio Missions NHP	516,440	$31,603.9	458	$13,571.2	$24,320.4	$40,350.3
San Francisco Maritime NHP	1,677,341	$58,951.9	689	$28,892.4	$44,985.9	$69,718.9
San Juan NHS	1,075,045	$65,787.9	785	$30,869.0	$51,491.7	$79,601.6
San Juan Island NHP	219,357	$13,423.7	160	$5,996.2	$10,728.7	$16,566.1
Sand Creek Massacre NHS	3,683	$225.4	3	$55.1	$111.3	$210.8
Santa Monica Mountains NRA	442,219	$23,052.3	303	$12,115.3	$19,664.1	$31,512.9
Saratoga NHP	48,457	$2,965.4	38	$1,120.9	$2,155.0	$3,455.2
Saugus Iron Works NHS	9,753	$596.9	8	$264.8	$456.5	$751.6
Scotts Bluff NM	102,913	$6,297.8	86	$2,179.5	$3,787.9	$6,665.4
Sequoia NP*	1,015,590	$75,491.8	916	$27,665.8	$49,732.3	$82,531.3
Shenandoah NP	1,145,329	$75,221.7	937	$37,242.5	$60,603.6	$93,850.3
Shiloh NMP	493,601	$30,206.2	450	$9,219.8	$17,577.3	$32,711.9
Sitka NHP	195,158	$39,879.4	955	$26,147.8	$40,611.4	$65,875.7
Sleeping Bear Dunes NL*	1,314,054	$147,937.8	2,741	$69,735.1	$123,187.0	$217,642.6
Springfield Armory NHS	14,262	$872.7	11	$418.4	$711.5	$1,103.9
Statue Of Liberty NM	2,544,733	$155,726.3	1,790	$85,204.4	$137,865.5	$201,483.7
Steamtown NHS*	87,704	$4,957.8	71	$2,235.0	$3,763.7	$6,144.5
Stones River NB	218,851	$13,392.7	194	$6,293.6	$10,385.0	$17,150.6
Sunset Crater Volcano NM	149,346	$9,139.3	117	$3,276.7	$5,574.0	$9,446.4
Tallgrass Prairie NPRES	15,890	$972.5	14	$373.1	$661.7	$1,153.9
Thaddeus Kosciuszko NMEM	1,718	$105.1	1	$57.1	$90.6	$145.0
Theodore Roosevelt NP	600,867	$36,951.1	464	$11,776.3	$20,399.5	$36,549.0
Theodore Roosevelt Birthplace NHS	15,061	$921.7	11	$503.2	$816.6	$1,194.7
Theodore Roosevelt Inaugural NHS	15,856	$970.3	12	$353.3	$728.6	$1,146.6
Theodore Roosevelt Island P	125,793	$7,698.0	100	$3,963.2	$6,418.6	$9,890.1
Thomas Edison NHP	44,145	$2,701.5	31	$1,483.2	$2,387.2	$3,504.9
Thomas Jefferson NMEM	2,177,039	$41,617.7	549	$22,175.0	$36,576.6	$56,475.9
Thomas Stone NHS	5,397	$330.3	4	$171.0	$275.5	$421.6
Timpanogos Cave NM	99,762	$6,105.0	95	$2,988.5	$4,866.5	$8,459.4
Timucuan EHP	904,101	$55,326.9	792	$25,146.3	$43,438.8	$71,149.7
Tonto NM	43,580	$2,666.9	38	$1,375.8	$2,238.0	$3,583.7
Tumacácori NHP	29,532	$1,807.3	25	$723.0	$1,222.2	$2,052.3
Tuskegee Airmen NHS	19,921	$1,219.1	18	$445.1	$763.2	$1,380.4
Tuskegee Institute NHS	20,186	$1,235.2	18	$451.0	$773.4	$1,398.7
Tuzigoot NM	81,805	$5,006.2	71	$2,569.7	$4,152.9	$6,620.1
Ulysses S Grant NHS	33,072	$2,023.9	31	$1,019.0	$1,676.0	$2,843.7
Upper Delaware NSR&NRR	178,910	$9,014.7	94	$4,485.2	$7,078.4	$10,304.3
Valley Forge NHP	1,212,219	$74,130.6	1,053	$40,230.4	$63,902.5	$102,553.3
Vanderbilt Mansion NHS	355,410	$21,749.5	262	$10,578.1	$17,915.0	$26,836.7

Table 6. (Continued)

Park Unit	Non-Local Recreation Visits	Non-Local Visitor Spending ($000s)	Impact of Non-Local Visitor Spending			
			Jobs	Labor Income ($000s)	Value Added ($000s)	Output ($000s)
Vicksburg NMP	481,540	$29,468.1	434	$12,087.0	$20,492.7	$35,899.9
Vietnam Veterans MEM	3,686,040	$70,464.8	930	$37,545.5	$61,929.5	$95,621.9
Virgin Islands NP*	483,341	$69,936.8	875	$37,046.7	$64,945.3	$100,042.9
Voyageurs NP	204,776	$15,926.1	222	$5,014.5	$10,231.3	$17,638.3
Walnut Canyon NM	93,028	$5,692.9	73	$2,041.1	$3,472.1	$5,884.2
War In The Pacific NHP	214,975	$13,155.5	168	$6,686.2	$10,868.9	$16,812.0
Washington Monument	0	$0.0	0	$0.0	$0.0	$0.0
Washita Battlefield NHS	8,917	$545.7	7	$170.6	$307.5	$557.4
Weir Farm NHS	18,030	$1,103.4	13	$596.4	$973.6	$1,416.9
Whiskeytown NRA	563,180	$28,804.0	379	$9,528.8	$17,910.0	$31,080.8
White House	547,315	$10,462.8	138	$5,574.9	$9,195.5	$14,198.2
White Sands NM*	410,711	$21,502.3	272	$6,868.5	$12,847.2	$22,436.1
Whitman Mission NHS	51,059	$3,124.6	40	$970.6	$1,959.1	$3,316.0
William Howard Taft NHS	16,309	$998.1	15	$448.3	$763.0	$1,308.5
Wilson's Creek NB	140,452	$8,595.1	132	$3,492.1	$5,850.4	$10,421.6
Wind Cave NP*	521,150	$48,870.4	787	$18,238.3	$33,005.6	$59,247.2
Wolf Trap NP for the Performing Arts	358,676	$21,949.4	285	$11,280.3	$18,287.9	$28,238.0
Women's Rights NHP*	29,585	$1,973.2	23	$641.5	$1,461.8	$2,302.5
World War II Memorial	3,467,163	$66,280.6	875	$35,316.0	$58,252.1	$89,943.8
World War II Valor in the Pacific NM	1,471,028	$90,020.4	1,075	$42,239.4	$70,458.3	$108,922.2
Wrangell - St Elias NP&PRES	87,158	$125,890.9	1,754	$62,891.0	$105,606.3	$175,299.6
Wright Brothers NMEM	392,125	$23,996.3	347	$9,485.9	$16,352.0	$27,882.7
Wupatki NM	169,146	$10,351.0	133	$3,759.7	$6,374.4	$10,784.1
Yellowstone NP*	3,341,357	$398,352.3	5,594	$164,260.6	$270,769.2	$470,933.5
Yosemite NP*	3,698,789	$373,489.6	5,097	$159,765.9	$281,241.6	$467,053.8
Yukon - Charley Rivers NPRES	1,393	$1,603.5	18	$813.7	$1,453.8	$2,335.5
Zion NP*	2,769,253	$149,672.2	1,825	$75,300.7	$123,411.4	$190,531.5

*For these parks, results are based on a visitor survey at the designated park. For other parks, visitor characteristics and spending averages are adapted from national averages for each park type.

Table 7. Visits, spending and economic contributions to state economies of NPS visitor spending

State	Total Recreation Visits	Total Visitor Spending ($ Millions)	Contribution of all Visitor Spending			
			Jobs	Labor Income ($ Millions)	Value Added ($ Millions)	Output ($Millions)
Alabama	717,724	$26.5	381	$10.0	$16.5	$29.0
Alaska	2,412,524	$1,061.7	16,181	$544.3	$889.7	$1,452.4
Arizona	9,979,972	$745.6	11,470	$395.0	$651.2	$1,044.8
Arkansas	2,727,454	$138.9	2,014	$51.9	$91.0	$162.6
California	36,011,297	$1,533.7	20,287	$824.2	$1,329.5	$2,133.4
Colorado	5,811,546	$347.4	4,991	$184.5	$297.1	$483.5
Connecticut	21,465	$1.2	14	$0.6	$0.9	$1.4
Delaware	0	$0.0	0	$0.0	$0.0	$0.0
District of Columbia	34,286,073	$596.7	5,553	$272.0	$432.9	$614.6
Florida	10,366,612	$572.6	8,064	$289.8	$491.6	$788.4
Georgia	7,350,309	$354.8	5,287	$171.2	$285.4	$476.1
Hawaii	5,119,035	$314.5	3,723	$146.4	$247.7	$381.2
Idaho	553,554	$25.5	398	$10.1	$16.8	$30.9
Illinois	295,464	$16.5	218	$8.1	$14.5	$22.7
Indiana	2,148,903	$88.5	1,273	$34.3	$59.1	$102.6
Iowa	207,352	$11.5	176	$4.5	$7.8	$13.9
Kansas	101,752	$4.6	64	$1.7	$3.1	$5.4
Kentucky	1,717,853	$103.3	1,479	$40.8	$72.3	$124.4
Louisiana	625,913	$33.7	471	$14.3	$24.6	$41.0
Maine	2,431,052	$200.9	3,138	$92.7	$154.6	$268.5
Maryland	6,658,643	$217.2	2,770	$99.8	$170.8	$266.1
Massachusetts	10,487,447	$503.2	6,499	$255.3	$407.5	$629.5
Michigan	2,192,477	$181.7	2,819	$85.9	$148.4	$254.3
Minnesota	601,274	$34.4	501	$15.4	$27.7	$46.2
Mississippi	6,449,713	$191.4	2,436	$65.5	$110.2	$186.6
Missouri	4,171,826	$297.7	4,982	$149.6	$238.2	$409.9
Montana	4,451,755	$403.4	6,525	$179.5	$288.7	$526.5
Nebraska	304,046	$13.2	200	$5.3	$8.9	$16.0
Nevada	4,808,929	$194.1	2,194	$86.5	$140.1	$214.6
New Hampshire	33,663	$1.5	27	$0.8	$1.4	$2.2
New Jersey	4,885,202	$153.0	2,275	$85.1	$133.7	$201.9
New Mexico	1,502,808	$81.1	1,123	$31.0	$51.7	$90.9
New York	12,627,820	$446.4	4,885	$206.1	$348.7	$509.6
North Carolina	17,706,033	$1,110.3	16,703	$504.6	$854.8	$1,461.9
North Dakota	669,242	$39.2	528	$13.9	$24.9	$43.5
Ohio	2,611,158	$156.7	2,437	$71.9	$122.4	$211.2
Oklahoma	1,497,654	$22.7	234	$6.8	$10.8	$18.6
Oregon	875,271	$58.5	924	$29.0	$46.4	$80.7
Pennsylvania	8,768,869	$444.4	6,848	$223.9	$358.4	$600.1
Rhode Island	51,944	$2.8	35	$1.2	$2.1	$3.3

Table 7. (Continued)

State	Total Recreation Visits	Total Visitor Spending ($ Millions)	Contribution of all Visitor Spending			
			Jobs	Labor Income ($ Millions)	Value Added ($ Millions)	Output ($Millions)
South Carolina	1,566,756	$80.3	1,158	$32.9	$56.1	$95.6
South Dakota	3,950,666	$236.4	3,706	$87.0	$154.7	$284.0
Tennessee	8,414,094	$541.0	7,868	$255.1	$431.6	$713.9
Texas	3,939,160	$188.1	2,592	$87.1	$150.2	$247.2
Utah	9,503,305	$613.7	9,416	$295.9	$492.9	$861.3
Vermont	32,403	$1.7	25	$0.7	$1.2	$2.1
Virginia	23,398,517	$926.3	13,256	$429.9	$714.8	$1,176.0
Washington	7,529,549	$419.2	5,164	$181.3	$337.8	$531.2
West Virginia	1,543,425	$63.4	863	$23.3	$38.3	$66.3
Wisconsin	273,933	$28.4	442	$12.6	$21.2	$37.4
Wyoming	6,194,752	$721.0	9,372	$272.7	$483.1	$831.2
America Samoa	10,440	$0.6	7	$0.3	$0.4	$0.7
Guam	255,923	$13.8	176	$7.0	$11.3	$17.4
Puerto Rico	1,279,814	$68.9	823	$32.1	$53.5	$82.7
Virgin Islands	645,956	$78.8	980	$41.1	$71.8	$110.6

Table 8. Visits, spending and economic contributions to regional economies of NPS visitor spending

Region	Total Recreation Visits	Total Visitor Spending ($ Millions)	Contribution of all Visitor Spending			
			Jobs	Labor Income ($ Millions)	Value Added ($ Millions)	Output ($ Millions)
Alaska	2,412,524	$1,061.7	16,181	$544.3	$889.7	$1,452.4
Intermountain	41,274,385	$3,058.1	45,685	$1,567.9	$2,670.8	$4,446.8
Midwest	20,255,547	$1,247.8	19,951	$629.6	$1,086.1	$1,878.2
National Capital	49,525,528	$928.6	12,404	$485.0	$790.7	$1,221.9
Northeast	49,863,293	$2,283.6	32,141	$1,263.3	$2,091.7	$3,287.0
Pacific West	56,770,565	$2,624.8	35,284	$1,425.8	$2,326.9	$3,736.4
Southeast	62,678,479	$3,508.0	52,627	$1,758.3	$3,020.5	$5,054.9

Table 9. Visit allocation to states for multi-state parks

Park Unit	**State**	**Share**
Assateague Island NS	Maryland	33%
Assateague Island NS	Virginia	67%
Big South Fork NRRA	Kentucky	41%
Big South Fork NRRA	Tennessee	59%
Bighorn Canyon NRA	Montana	54%
Park Unit	**State**	**Share**

Bighorn Canyon NRA	Wyoming	46%
Blue Ridge PKWY	North Carolina	62%
Blue Ridge PKWY	Virginia	38%
Chesapeake & Ohio Canal NHP	District of Columbia	24%
Chesapeake & Ohio Canal NHP	Maryland	76%
Chickamauga & Chattanooga NMP	Georgia	50%
Chickamauga & Chattanooga NMP	Tennessee	50%
Cumberland Gap NHP	Kentucky	93%
Cumberland Gap NHP	Virginia	7%
Delaware Water Gap NRA	New Jersey	71%
Delaware Water Gap NRA	Pennsylvania	29%
Dinosaur NM	Colorado	74%
Dinosaur NM	Utah	26%
Gateway NRA	New Jersey	20%
Gateway NRA	New York	80%
Glen Canyon NRA	Arizona	8%
Glen Canyon NRA	Utah	92%
Great Smoky Mountains NP	North Carolina	44%
Great Smoky Mountains NP	Tennessee	56%
Gulf Islands NS	Florida	75%
Gulf Islands NS	Mississippi	25%
Hovenweep NM	Colorado	44%
Hovenweep NM	Utah	56%
Lake Mead NRA	Arizona	25%
Lake Mead NRA	Nevada	75%
Natchez Trace PKWY	Alabama	7%
Natchez Trace PKWY	Mississippi	80%
Natchez Trace PKWY	Tennessee	13%
National Capital Parks East	District of Columbia	90%
National Capital Parks East	Maryland	10%
Saint Croix NSR	Minnesota	50%
Saint Croix NSR	Wisconsin	50%
Upper Delaware NSR&NRR	New York	50%
Upper Delaware NSR&NRR	Pennsylvania	50%
Yellowstone NP	Montana	51%
Yellowstone NP	Wyoming	49%

End Notes

[1] The economic region for parks in Alaska and Hawaii are defined as the State of Alaska and the State of Hawaii, respectively. Due to data limitations, the island economy of the State of Hawaii is used as a surrogate economic region for the U.S. territories of America Samoa, Puerto Rico, and the Virgin Islands.

[2] This method results in some relatively large local gateway regions, especially in some western states where counties are large. Because of this, there is the potential for including some areas that are not intrinsically linked to the local economies surrounding each park.

[3] Parks count visits as the number of individuals who enter the park each day. For example, a family of four taking a week-long vacation to Yellowstone National Park and staying at a lodge outside of the park would be counted as 28 visits (4 individuals who enter the park on 7 different days). A different family of four, also taking a week-long vacation to Yellowstone National Park but lodging within the park, would be counted as 4 visits (4 individuals who enter the park on a single day and then stay within the park for the remainder of their trip). These differences are a result of the realities of the limitations in the methods available to count park visits.

In: Economic Contributions of National Park ... ISBN: 978-1-60876-005-3
Editor: Jenell Meehan

Chapter 2

ECONOMIC BENEFITS TO LOCAL COMMUNITIES FROM NATIONAL PARK VISITATION, 2011*

Yue Cui, Ed Mahoney and Teresa Herbowicz

EXECUTIVE SUMMARY

The National Park System received 278.9 million recreation visits in 2011. Park visitors spent $12.95 billion in local gateway regions (within roughly 60 miles of the park). Visitors staying overnight outside the park (in motels, hotels, cabins, and bed and breakfasts) accounted for 54.9% of the total spending. About half (48%) of the spending was for lodging and meals, 21.4% for gas and local transportation, 9.7% for recreation and entertainment, 8.1% for groceries, and 12.7% for other retail purchases.

The contribution of this park visitor spending to the national economy amounted to 251,600 jobs, $9.34 billion in labor income, and $16.50 billion in value added[1]. The direct effects of visitor spending are measured at the local level in gateway regions around national parks. Local economic impacts were estimated after excluding spending by park visitors from the local area (9.8% of the total spending). Combining local impacts across all parks yielded a total local impact (including direct and secondary effects) of 162,400 jobs, $4.58

---

* This is an edited, reformatted and augmented version of Natural Resource Report NPS/NRSS/ARD/NRR—2013/632, issued by the National Park Service, February 2013.

billion in labor income, and $8.15 billion value added. The four local economic sectors most directly affected by non-local visitor spending are lodging, restaurants, retail trade, and recreation and entertainment. Their spending supported 45,200 jobs in restaurants and bars, 34,100 jobs in lodging sectors, 15,500 jobs in retail and wholesale trade, and 20,000 jobs in recreation and entertainment.

In this 2011 study, payroll impacts were not included due to the conversion to a new accounting system for the National Park Service, which prevented obtaining the required inputs for such analysis in time for publication.

INTRODUCTION

This report provides updated estimates of National Park Service (NPS) visitor spending for 2011 and estimates the economic impacts of visitor spending. Visitor spending and impacts are estimated using the Money Generation Model version 2 (MGM2) (Stynes et al. 2000) based on park visits (also called recreation visits) during the calendar year 2011, spending averages from park visitor surveys, and local-area and national-level economic multipliers.

Visitor spending effects are estimated for all park units with visitation data. Direct effects cover businesses selling goods and services directly to park visitors. Secondary effects include: indirect effects resulting from sales to backward-linked industries within the local region, and induced effects from household spending of income earned directly or indirectly from visitor spending. Impacts of construction activity and park purchases of goods and services are not included.

Effects are estimated at both the national and local level. Most spending directly associated with park visits occurs in gateway regions around each park. Impacts of this spending on the local economies are estimated using local input-output models for each park. Local regions are defined as a 60-mile radius[2] around each park. To estimate impacts on the national economy, spending within roughly 60 miles of the park is applied to the national input-output model. System-wide totals covering impacts on local economies are also estimated by summing the spending and local impact estimates for all park units. Results for individual park units are reported in the Appendix.

2011 UPDATES

The 2011 estimates reflect new visitor surveys at four parks. In 2011, visitor surveys were conducted at Joshua Tree NP, Chiricahua NM, Fort Bowie NHS and Fort Stanwix NM.[3] Spending and visitor profiles for these parks were updated based upon the survey data. For other parks, spending profiles from 2010 were price-adjusted to 2011 using Bureau of Labor Statistics consumer price indices for each spending category. Consumer prices remained fairly stable between 2010 and 2011 except for an increase of 26% in gasoline prices and a 10% increase in transportation costs.

Visitor segment mixes were assumed to be unchanged except as reflected in overnight stays or new visitor surveys. Except for parks with new visitor surveys, average party sizes, lengths of stay and reentry factors were assumed to be unchanged from 2010. Visit and overnight stay figures for all parks were updated to 2011 from the NPS public use statistics (Street 2012).

Multipliers for individual parks were estimated in 2011 based on 2008 IMPLAN data and IMPLAN's trade flow models (Stynes, 2011). Local regions were defined to include all counties within roughly 60 road miles of each park. For 2011, local region multipliers were adjusted from 2008 to 2010 based on structural changes in the national economy (i.e., ratios of jobs, income and value added to sales in each sector). Secondary effects and direct job ratios were adjusted to 2011 based on consumer price indices.

RECREATION VISITS

The National Park System received 278.9 million recreation visits in 2011. Spending by visitors was estimated by dividing all visitors to each park into segments with distinct spending patterns and applying spending averages based on surveys of park visitors at selected parks. As spending averages are measured on a party-day basis (party nights for overnight trips), the NPS counts of recreation visits are converted from person entries to a park to party-days in the area by applying average party size, length of stay, and park re-entry factors. This eliminates some double counting of visits. To the extent possible, spending not directly related to a park visit is excluded.[4]

In 2011, there were 13.75 million recreation overnight stays in the parks. Twenty-nine percent of park visits were day trips by local residents, 40.0% were day trips from 60 miles or more,[5] and 27.7% involved an overnight stay near the park. Visitor spending depends on the number of days spent in the local area and the type of lodging for overnight trips. Day trips by non-local visitors accounted for 33.5% of the party days spent in the local area, day trips by local visitors, for 27.8%, and overnight stays, for 38.7%. Sixty-four percent of all overnight stays by park visitors were in hotels, motels, lodges, or bed and breakfasts outside the park; another 17.5% were in campgrounds outside the park, 7.5% in private homes; and 11.1% were inside the park in NPS campgrounds, lodges, or back-country sites resided in National Parks.

VISITOR SPENDING

Visitor spending averages cover expenses within the local region, excluding park entry fees. Spending averages for each segment are derived from park visitor surveys at selected parks over the past ten years. Bureau of Labor Statistics price indices for each spending category are applied to adjust all spending to 2011 dollars.

NPS system-wide spending averages for 2011 are given in Table 1 for seven distinct visitor segments. A typical park visitor party of local residents on a day trip spends $49.86 and $75.02 if a non-local party (Table 1).

On a party-night basis, spending by visitors on overnight trips varied from $59.91 for back-country campers to $330.70 for visitors staying in park lodges. Campers spent $119.86 per night, if staying outside the park, and $86.72, if staying inside the park. Spending averages at individual parks varied from these system-wide averages due to differences in local prices and spending opportunities.

In total, park visitors spent $12.95 billion in the local region surrounding the parks in 2011.[6] Local residents accounted for 9.8% of this spending (Table 2). Visitors staying in motels and lodges outside the park accounted for 54.9% of the total spending, while non-local visitors on day trips contributed 20.5% of all spending.

Expenses at lodging and restaurants/bars accounted for about a quarter of the spending, each. Expenses on transportation (mainly auto fuel) accounted for 21.4%, groceries 8.1%, other retail purchases 12.8%, and recreation and entertainment 9.7% (Figure 1).

Table 1. National Park Visitor Spending in the Local Area by Segment, 2011 ($ per party per day/night)

	Visitor Segment						
Spending category	Local Day Trip	Non-local Day Trip	NPS Lodge	NPS Camp Ground	NPS Back-country	Motel- Outside Park	CampOutside Park
Motel, hotel, B&B	-	-	151.89	0.31	5.25	92.67	0.12
Camping fees	-	-	0.39	15.30	2.44	0.11	25.16
Restaurants & bars	14.75	19.50	73.79	11.85	8.42	58.35	16.23
Recreation & entertainment	4.83	8.73	22.11	7.29	5.85	17.67	15.10
Groceries	7.27	7.14	12.56	14.63	6.43	14.39	12.36
Gas & oil	12.92	23.96	31.67	24.93	19.17	25.72	29.18
Local transportation	0.11	1.34	6.44	1.34	0.28	3.14	0.89
Retail purchases	9.97	14.34	31.85	11.07	12.07	27.08	20.82
Total	49.86	75.02	330.70	86.72	59.91	239.13	119.86

Note: Columns may not sum to totals due to rounding.

Table 2. National Park Visitor Spending by Segment, 2011

Segment	Total Spending ($ Millions)	Percent of Spending
Local day trip	1,264	9.8%
Non-local day trip	2,659	20.5%
Lodge/cabin-in park	376	2.9%
Camp-in park	301	2.3%
NPS back-country campers	37	0.3%
Motel-outside park	7,105	54.9%
Camp-outside park	871	6.7%
Other overnight visitors [a]	339	2.6%
Total	12,952	100.0%

[a] Other overnight visitors include visitors staying overnight in the area but not incurring lodging costs.

Notes: Columns may not sum to totals due to rounding.

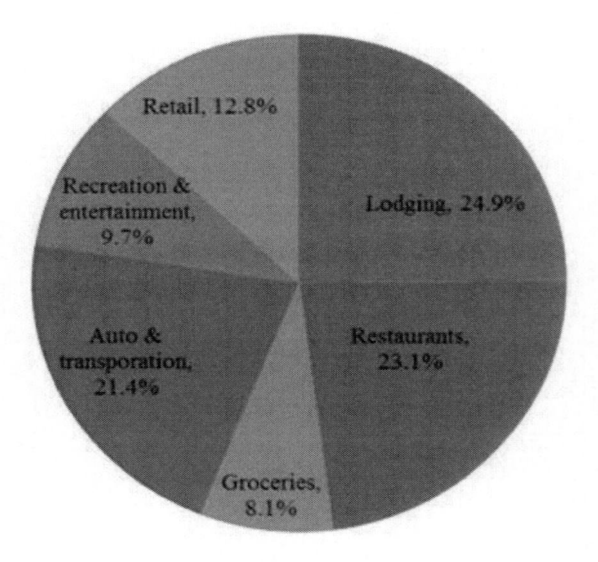

Figure 1. Distribution of National Park Visitor Spending in 2011.

LOCAL SIGNIFICANCE AND IMPACTS OF VISITOR SPENDING

Local economic significance and economic impacts of visitor spending are estimated in the MGM2 model using multipliers for local areas around each park. Multipliers capture both the direct and secondary economic effects in gateway regions around the parks in terms of jobs, labor income, and value added. National totals are calculated as the sum of the local impacts for 374 park units that have counts of visitors. Both economic significance and economic impacts were estimated for local areas. The average sales multiplier across all parks' local regions is 1.43. For every dollar of direct sales another $0.43 in sales is generated in the local region through secondary effects.

Economic Significance

The economic *significance* estimates in Table 3 measure the effects of all visitor spending ($12.95 billion), including that of local visitors.

The $12.95 billion spent by park visitors within 60 miles of the park in 2011 (Table 2) had a total economic effect (significance) of $14.99 billion in sales, $5.04 billion in labor income, and $8.94 billion in value added. Visitor spending supported about 177,500 jobs in gateway regions. Total effects may be divided between the direct effects that occur in local businesses selling goods and services directly to park visitors and secondary effects that result from the circulation of this money within the local economy.[7]

Direct effects were $9.74 billion in sales, $3.29 billion in labor income, $5.66 billion in value added, and 135,300 jobs. The local regions captured 75.2% of all visitor spending as direct sales. Note that direct sales of $9.74 billion is less than the $12.95 billion in visitor spending as most of the manufacturing share of retail purchases (groceries, gas, sporting goods, souvenirs) is not included. It is assumed that most of the producer price of retail purchases immediately leaks out of the region to cover the cost of goods sold. Sales figures for retail and wholesale trade are the margins on retail purchases.

Economic Impacts

The economic *impacts* (which exclude spending by local visitors) in Table 4 measure the effects of the $11.69 billion spent by visitors who did not reside within the gateway regions. Economic impact measures estimate the likely losses in economic activity to the region in the absence of the park. Should the park opportunities not be available, it is assumed that local residents would spend the money on other local activities, while visitors from outside the region would not have made a trip to the region.[8] Spending by local residents on visits to the park does not represent "new money" to the region and is therefore generally excluded when estimating impacts. Local resident spending is included in the economic significance measures, as these capture all economic activity associated with park visits, including local and non-local visitors.

Table 3. Economic Significance of National Park Visitor Spending to Local Economies, 2011

Sector/Spending category	Sales ($ Millions)	Jobs	Labor Income ($ Millions)	Value Added ($ Millions)
Direct Effects				
Motel, hotel cabin or B&B	2,979	29,552	836	1,694
Camping fees	244	4,541	77	150
Restaurants & bars	2,991	51,435	1,089	1,653
Recreation & entertainment	1,255	22,331	418	784
Other vehicle expenses	173	2,009	88	102
Local transportation	315	6,522	158	242
Grocery stores	279	4,770	140	204
Gas stations	114	1,401	48	80
Other retail	583	10,500	273	423
Wholesale trade	266	1,570	114	206
Local manufacturing	537	685	48	118
Total Direct Effects	9,736	135,316	3,289	5,656
Secondary Effects	5,256	42,194	1,753	3,279
Total Effects	14,992	177,510	5,042	8,935

Notes: Economic significance covers all $12.95 billion in spending by park visitors in the local region, including that of local visitors. Columns may not sum to totals due to rounding.

Excluding $1.26 billion dollars spent by local visitors (Table 2) reduced the total spending to $11.69 billion for the impact analysis. Local visitors represented about 29.1% of all visits but less than 10% of all visitors' spending (Table 2). The total effects of visitor spending, excluding locals, was $13.66 billion in sales, $4.58 billion in labor income, $8.15 billion in value added, and 162,400 jobs. The economic sectors most directly affected by non-local visitors to the parks are lodging, restaurants, retail trade, and recreation and entertainment. Non-local visitor spending supported 45,200 jobs in restaurants and bars, 34,100 jobs in lodging sectors, 15,500 jobs in retail and wholesale trade, and 20,000 jobs in recreation and entertainment.

Table 4. Economic Impacts of National Park Visitor Spending on Local Economies, 2011

Sector/Spending category	Sales ($ Millions)	Jobs	Labor Income ($ Millions)	Value Added ($ Millions)
Direct Effects				
Motel, hotel cabin or B&B	2,979	29,552	836	1,694
Camping fees	244	4,541	77	150
Restaurants & bars	2,616	45,161	951	1,444
Recreation & entertainment	1,122	20,033	375	701
Other vehicle expenses	158	1,843	81	93
Local transportation	312	6,451	156	240
Grocery stores	229	3,950	115	167
Gas stations	98	1,214	41	69
Other retail	502	9,072	234	363
Wholesale trade	220	1,314	93	170
Local manufacturing	417	539	37	91
Total Direct Effects	8,897	123,670	2,996	5,182
Secondary Effects	4,762	38,753	1,582	2,965
Total Effects	13,659	162,423	4,578	8,147

Note: Economic impacts cover the $11.69 billion spent by non-local visitors. Columns may not sum to totals due to rounding.

NATIONAL SIGNIFICANCE OF VISITOR SPENDING

The contribution of NPS visitor spending to the national economy can be estimated by applying the spending totals to multipliers for the national economy. This circulates spending that occurs within gateway regions around national parks within the broader national economy, capturing impacts on sectors that manufacture goods purchased by park visitors and additional secondary effects. The estimates do not include park visitors' spending at home on durable goods such as camping, hunting and fishing equipment, recreation vehicles, boats, and other goods used on trips to the national parks. The estimates also exclude airfares and other en-route spending that occurs more than 60 miles from the park. Since many long-distance trips involve multiple purposes and often visits to multiple parks, it is difficult to capture these expenses without double counting or attributing spending not directly related to a national park visit. With the above exclusions, the contribution of visitor spending to the national economy in 2011 was $30.09 billion in sales,

251,600 jobs, $9.34 billion in labor income, and $16.50 billion in value added (Table 5).

Table 5. Economic Significance of National Park Visitor Spending to National Economy, 2011

Sector/Spending category	Sales ($ Millions)	Jobs	Labor Income ($ Millions)	Value Added ($ Millions)
Direct Effects				
Motel, hotel, cabin or B&B	2,979	27,690	876	1,730
Camping fees	244	4,306	81	153
Restaurants & bars	2,991	52,937	1,059	1,628
Recreation & entertainment	1,255	22,153	418	785
Other vehicle expenses	173	1,996	90	103
Local transportation	315	6,492	175	250
Grocery stores	279	4,817	142	204
Gas stations	114	1,518	47	80
Other retail	583	10,510	276	425
Wholesale trade	468	2,637	205	365
Local manufacturing	2,858	4,121	291	711
Total Direct Effects	12,259	139,177	3,660	6,434
Secondary Effects	17,826	112,466	5,682	10,067
Total Effects	30,085	251,643	9,342	16,501

Note: Columns may not sum to totals due to rounding.

With the exception of manufacturing activity and a portion of activity in wholesale trade, the direct effects of visitor spending accrue to local regions around national parks.[9] Compared to the contribution to local economies (Table 3), an additional 74,100 jobs are supported nationally by NPS visitor spending, primarily due to the greater indirect and induced effects at the national level. The sales multiplier for NPS visitor spending at the national level is 2.51, compared to an average of 1.43 for local regions around national parks.

STATE AND REGIONAL IMPACTS OF VISITOR SPENDING

Economic impacts of individual parks can be aggregated to the state level with a few complications. While most parks fall within a single state, there are 20 park units with facilities in more than one state. For these parks, shares of visits were assigned to each state based on percentages provided by the NPS

Public Use Statistics Office. It was assumed that spending and economic impacts are proportional to where recreation visits are assigned.

Estimates of park visits, spending, and *state-level* economic impacts for each state and U.S. territory are given in Table A-2 in the Appendix. These state estimates are larger than the impacts for local economies since states generally include a larger economic productive capacity than local areas and therefore account for a larger share of the overall impacts.

Estimates of park visits, spending, and *regional-level* economic impacts for each NPS region are given in Table A-3 in the Appendix. Similar to the state-level impacts discussed above, these regional estimates are larger than the impacts for state economies since regions generally include a larger economic productive capacity than states and therefore account for a larger share of the overall impacts. As noted earlier, impacts reported here do not include long-distance travel, airfares, or purchases made at home for items that may be used on trips to national parks.

METHODS

Spending and impacts were estimated using the MGM2 model. NPS public use statistics for calendar year 2011 provide estimates of the number of park visits and overnight stays at each park. For each park, recreation visits were allocated to the seven MGM2 segments,[10] converted to party days/nights spent in the local area and then multiplied by per-day spending averages for each segment. Spending and impact estimates for 2011 are made individually for each park unit and then summed to obtain national totals for impacts on local regions. Impacts on the national economy are also estimated by applying all visitor spending to multipliers for the national economy.

Spending averages cover all trip expenses within roughly 60 miles of the park. They therefore exclude most en route expenses on longer trips, as well as airfares and purchases made at home in preparation for the trip, including costs of durable goods and equipment. Spending averages vary from park to park based on the type of park and the regional setting (low, medium, or high spending area).

The segment mix is very important in estimating visitor spending, as spending varies considerably across the MGM2 segments. Segment shares are estimated based on park overnight stay data and, where available, park visitor surveys. For park units that lack recent visitor surveys, estimates are made by generalizing from studies at similar parks or based on manager or researcher judgment.

For parks with VSP (Visitor Services Project) studies over the past ten years, spending averages are estimated from the visitor survey data collected at each park.[11] Averages estimated in the surveys were price-adjusted to 2011 using Bureau of Labor Statistics (BLS) price indices for each spending category. Sampling errors for the spending averages in VSP studies are generally 5–10% overall and can be as high as 20% for individual visitor segments (Stynes, 2011).

The observed spending patterns in park visitor studies are then used to estimate spending averages for other parks that lack visitor spending surveys. This procedure does not capture some spending variations attributable to unique characteristics of a given park or gateway region—for example, the wider use of public transportation at Alaska parks or extra expenses for special commercial attractions in or around some parks, such as rafting trips, air overflights, and other tours. When visitor studies are conducted at individual parks, these unique situations are taken into account.

Multipliers for local regions around national parks were applied to the visitor spending totals to translate spending into jobs, income, and value added and also to estimate secondary effects. All MGM2 multipliers were re-estimated in 2011 using IMPLAN ver 3.0 and 2008 economic data (Minnesota IMPLAN Group 2009). The multipliers were adjusted to 2011 based on structural changes in the national IMPLAN models between 2008 and 2010 and price changes between 2010 and 2011.

Based on national IMPLAN models, there were some significant structural changes in economic ratios and multipliers between 2008 and 2010. Most notable was a change in ratios for the recreation and entertainment sector (IMPLAN sector 410) due to under estimated output in 2008. IMPLAN ratios in 2010 for sector 410 were triple the 2008 estimates. Using 2008 multiplier would cause a significant underestimate of jobs, income and value added in the MGM2 recreation and entertainment sector estimates if the ratio were not adjusted from 2008 to 2010. The MGM2 estimates of jobs, income and value added are sensitive to any changes in these ratios and multipliers.

With the exception of parks with new visitor surveys in 2011, no changes were made in party sizes, lengths of stay, or re-entry factors between 2010 and 2011. MGM2 model parameters for individual parks are adjusted over time as new park visitor studies are conducted or other relevant information becomes available.

The retail margin used to the estimate economic impacts on gasoline sales with national park visits in 2010 was 22.3% and 8.3% at wholesale (Stynes, 2011). In a more recent report by Oil Price Information Service (2012), the retail margin is about 5% of the retail price. Energy Almanac (2012) shows that the distribution of gasoline, including retail and wholesale cost and profit, was approximately 10% of the gasoline's retail price, the refinery sector was 75% of the price, and fuel tax comprised 15% of the retail price in 2011. The fuel taxes can be shifted to the refinery sector since this shift has relatively minor effect on job estimates because the refinery sector has a very small job-to-sales ratio. In addition, U.S. refineries are concentrated in a few geographic areas and would seldom be located in NPS economic impact areas. As a result, the gasoline margins used to estimate 2011 economic impacts of national parks were adjusted as follows: 90% went to the petroleum refining sector; 5%, to the wholesale trade sector; and 5%, to the retail sector. This 2011 adjustment reduced the estimation of local economic significance of spending on gasoline associated with national park visits by 5,800 jobs.

Spending and impact totals for states were developed from the 2011 estimates by summing the results for all units in a given state using the mailing address for the park to identify the state. Twenty parks have facilities in more than one state. For these parks, visitors and spending were allocated to individual states based on shares used by the NPS Public Use Statistics Office for allocating visits to states. For example, visits to Great Smoky Mountains NP were split 44% to North Carolina and 56% to Tennessee. It should be noted that these allocations may not fully account for where the spending and impacts occur. There are also many other parks with facilities in a single state but located within 60 miles of a state border. A portion of the spending and impacts for these parks may accrue to nearby states.

ERRORS AND LIMITATIONS

The accuracy of the spending and impact estimates rests largely on the input data, namely (1) public use recreation visit and overnight stay data; (2) party size, length of stay, and park re-entry conversion factors; (3) visitor segment shares; (4) spending averages; and (5) local area multipliers.

Public use data provides reasonably accurate estimates of visitor entries for most parks. Some visitors may be missed by the counting procedures, while others may be counted multiple times when they re-enter a park more than once on a single trip. Accurate estimates of park re-entries, party sizes, and lengths of stay in the area are needed to convert park entries to the number of visitors or party days in the region. Visitors staying overnight outside the park pose significant problems as they tend to be the greatest spenders and may enter the park several times during their stay. Similarly, visitors staying inside the park may enter and leave it several times during their stay and be counted each time as a distinct visit. Re-entry factors adjust for these problems to the extent possible.

For multi-purpose trips, it is difficult to determine what portion of the spending should be attributed to the park visit. This is especially a problem for historic sites and parks in urban areas or parks in multiple-attraction destinations. For parks with visitor surveys, the proportion of days and spending counted was decided based on stated trip purposes and the importance of the park in generating the trip to the region.

Parkways and urban parks present special difficulties for economic impact analyses. These units have some of the highest number of visits while posing the most difficult problems for estimating visits, spending, and impacts. The majority of visits to these types of units were assumed to be day trips by local or non-local visitors, and only one night of spending was counted for overnight trips. Due to the high numbers of visits at these units, small changes in assumed spending averages or segment mixes can swing the spending estimates by substantial amounts.

Clusters of parks within a single 60-mile area pose additional difficulties. For example, the many monuments and parks in the Washington, D.C. area each count visitors separately. Similar difficulties exist for clusters of parks in Boston, New York, and San Francisco. To avoid double counting of spending across many national capital parks, we must know how many times a visitor has been counted at park units during a trip to the Washington, D.C., area. For parks in the National Capital Region, we currently assume an average of 1.7 park visits are counted for day trips by local visitors, 3.4 visits for day trips by non-local visitors, and 5.1 park visits on overnight trips. The total of non-local visitor spending for the National Capital Region in 2010 was $1.17 billion. This is 14% of the Travel Industry Association's tourist spending estimate of $8.3 billion for Washington, D.C., in 2008 (USTA 2010).

NPS units in Alaska also pose special problems for economic analysis. Spending opportunities near Alaska parks are limited and for many visitors the park visit is part of a cruise or guided tour, frequently purchased as a package. Most visitors are on extended trips to Alaska, making it difficult to allocate expenses to a particular park visit. Lodging, vehicle rentals, and air expenses frequently occur in Anchorage, many miles from the park. Also, many Alaska parks are only accessible by air or boat, so spending profiles estimated from visitor surveys at parks in the lower 48 states do not apply well. Due to the prominence of cruise lines and package tours, special studies are required to estimate the proportion of visitor spending that stays in the local regions around national park units in Alaska. In this report, Alaska statewide multipliers are used to estimate impacts for parks in Alaska.

A visit to one or more national parks is an important part of the trip for most Alaska visitors. One could therefore argue to count a substantial portion of tourism spending in Alaska as related to national park visits. The U.S. Travel Association estimated tourist spending in Alaska at $2.1 billion in 2008 (USTA 2010). This is ten times what we have included as spending by park visitors in the local regions around Alaska national parks. Including spending in Alaska outside the local regions would significantly increase the estimates; however, deciding which spending to include would be somewhat subjective.

REFERENCES

Energy Almanac. 2012. The California Energy Almanac. Available at http://energyalmanac.ca.gov/gasoline/margins/index.php

Minnesota IMPLAN Group Inc. 2009. IMPLAN Pro Version 3.0, user's guide. Stillwater, Minnesota.

Oil Price Information Service. 2012. Public Company Rack-to-Retail Margins. Available at http://www.opisretail.com/images/press%20release%20 images/BrandMargins%20FirstHalf.pdf

Street, B. 2012. Statistical abstract: 2011. Natural Resource Data Series NPS/NRSS/EQD/NRDS-2012/422. National Park Service, Fort Collins, Colorado.

Stynes, D.J. 2011. Economic benefits to local communities from national park visitation and payroll, 2009. Natural Resources Report NPS/NRPC/ SSD/NRR –2011/281. National Park Service, Fort Collins, Colorado.

Stynes, D. J., D. B. Propst, W. H. Chang, and Y. Sun. 2000. Estimating regional economic impacts of park visitor spending: Money Generation Model Version 2 (MGM2). Department of Park, Recreation and Tourism Resources, Michigan State University, East Lansing, Michigan.

U.S. Travel Association (USTA). 2010. The power of travel, economic impact of travel and tourism. Available at http://www.poweroftravel.org /statistics/.

Table A-1. Local-Level Impacts of NPS Visitor Spending on Local Economies by Park, 2011

Park Unit	Public Use Data		Visitor Spending 2011		Impacts of Non-local Visitor Spending		
	2011 Recreation Visits	2011 Overnight Stays	All Visitors ($000's)	Non-local Visitors ($000's)	Jobs	Labor Income ($000's)	Value Added ($000's)
Abraham Lincoln Birthplace NHP	163,568	-	6,061	5,636	94	2,566	4,334
Acadia NP	2,374,645	153,798	186,180	183,325	2,970	72,808	126,167
Adams NHP	219,975	-	15,139	14,076	172	6,911	11,458
African Burial Ground NM	108,585	-	7,407	6,866	77	3,715	6,165
Agate Fossil Beds NM	11,617	-	760	754	12	225	406
Alibates Flint Quarries NM	3,214	-	170	158	2	48	93
Allegheny Portage Railroad NHS	118,410	-	6,268	5,828	88	1,958	3,700
Amistad NRA	1,436,759	32,078	44,428	38,658	522	9,975	20,428
Andersonville NHS	108,812	-	4,032	3,749	57	1,284	2,456
Andrew Johnson NHS	52,322	-	2,770	2,575	41	1,028	1,838
Aniakchak NM & PRES	57	156	21	21	-	7	13
Antietam NB	384,987	-	20,018	17,996	243	8,813	15,021
*Apostle Islands NL	176,040	24,014	20,929	20,477	358	6,946	12,383
Appomattox Court House NHP	258,917	-	13,707	12,744	186	4,256	8,079
*Arches NP	1,040,758	50,915	113,722	113,722	1,638	33,855	65,849
Arkansas Post NMEM	37,127	-	1,376	1,279	20	350	645
Arlington House The R.E. Lee ME	576,816	-	39,697	36,910	396	15,681	26,077
Assateague Island NS	2,105,419	74,712	151,195	143,513	1,957	48,550	93,783
Aztec Ruins NM	41,106	-	1,380	1,337	17	392	736
*Badlands NP	870,741	44,576	22,203	22,203	317	7,302	12,064

Park Unit	Public Use Data		Visitor Spending 2011		Impacts of Non-local Visitor Spending		
	2011 Recreation Visits	2011 Overnight Stays	All Visitors ($000's)	Non-local Visitors ($000's)	Jobs	Labor Income ($000's)	Value Added ($000's)
Bandelier NM	193,914	9,300	9,218	8,908	135	3,461	5,941
Bent's Old Fort NHS	26,842	-	995	925	12	220	468
Bering Land Bridge NPRES	1,890	1,503	652	652	7	219	392
Big Bend NP	361,862	148,799	16,703	15,914	225	4,508	9,167
Big Cypress NPRES	941,393	19,957	117,467	114,919	1,891	66,660	111,384
Big Hole NB	36,290	-	1,345	1,250	19	376	709
Big South Fork NRRA	606,579	57,071	26,116	22,752	343	5,322	10,777
Big Thicket NPRES	137,722	1,891	9,891	9,382	138	4,755	8,248
Bighorn Canyon NRA	201,010	9,278	6,261	5,463	80	1,930	3,383
Biscayne NP	476,077	13,985	34,317	33,927	416	14,322	24,337
Black Canyon of the Gunnison NP	168,336	18,118	8,436	8,022	106	2,108	4,448
Blue Ridge PKWY	15,382,447	132,863	340,085	310,686	4,379	73,568	145,708
Bluestone NSR	41,670	-	1,901	1,660	24	542	938
Booker T. Washington NM	24,030	-	1,272	1,183	18	414	795
Boston African American NHS	379,906	-	26,145	24,310	298	11,936	19,788
Boston NHP	2,546,156	-	93,996	90,797	1,144	47,138	78,167
Brown v. Board of Education NHS	16,886	-	894	831	13	355	610
Bryce Canyon NP	1,296,000	133,221	115,066	113,928	1,726	32,695	64,683
Buck Island Reef NM	28,223	3,920	2,018	1,921	29	490	991
Buffalo NR	1,169,802	80,954	38,232	33,636	468	10,396	18,482
Cabrillo NM	813,351	-	55,975	52,045	681	22,071	39,667
Canaveral NS	1,005,001	3,146	72,256	68,525	1,034	32,487	57,312
Cane River Creole NHP	26,996	-	1,429	1,329	20	390	752

Table A-1. (Continued)

Park Unit	Public Use Data		Visitor Spending 2011		Impacts of Non-local Visitor Spending		
	2011 Recreation Visits	2011 Overnight Stays	All Visitors ($000's)	Non-local Visitors ($000's)	Jobs	Labor Income ($000's)	Value Added ($000's)
Canyon de Chelly NM	828,145	43,362	43,314	40,318	515	10,790	21,559
Canyonlands NP	473,773	87,910	39,976	39,571	519	12,526	23,338
Cape Cod NS	4,454,771	20,246	174,980	138,812	1,739	56,607	102,574
Cape Hatteras NS	1,960,711	69,366	104,173	98,959	1,349	34,713	62,224
Cape Krusenstern NM	8,668	9,237	2,987	2,987	31	998	1,787
Cape Lookout NS	508,116	28,854	37,621	35,784	532	10,457	19,937
Capitol Reef NP	668,834	36,577	40,856	40,607	600	11,968	23,459
*Capulin Volcano NM	46,358	-	1,391	1,366	18	288	573
Carl Sandburg Home NHS	89,721	-	4,750	4,416	70	1,819	3,151
Carlsbad Caverns NP	365,000	107	21,256	20,720	299	5,771	10,646
Casa Grande Ruins NM	72,308	-	2,282	2,142	30	930	1,602
Castillo de San Marcos NM	741,042	-	50,999	47,418	590	16,962	30,206
Castle Clinton NM	3,985,366	-	81,538	56,980	571	23,915	39,008
Catoctin Mountain Park	264,460	29,348	14,393	13,459	143	5,623	9,347
Cedar Breaks NM	493,147	1,998	18,241	16,961	255	5,368	10,492
Chaco Culture NHP	39,175	14,990	1,111	1,072	14	306	536
Chamizal NMEM	113,817	-	7,833	7,283	110	2,747	5,260
Channel Islands NP	242,756	60,922	22,368	21,308	296	10,912	19,246
Charles Pinckney NHS	45,254	-	2,396	2,227	34	915	1,579
Chattahoochee River NRA	3,161,297	-	102,108	68,878	798	29,323	46,311

Park Unit	Public Use Data		Visitor Spending 2011		Impacts of Non-local Visitor Spending		
	2011 Recreation Visits	2011 Overnight Stays	All Visitors ($000's)	Non-local Visitors ($000's)	Jobs	Labor Income ($000's)	Value Added ($000's)
*Chesapeake & Ohio Canal NHP	3,937,504	7,690	54,008	33,909	435	16,885	28,105
Chickamauga & Chattanooga NMP	1,036,699	1,961	54,908	51,058	774	21,858	38,327
Chickasaw NRA	1,212,139	73,956	18,160	13,961	150	3,145	5,570
*Chiricahua NM	37,037	5,232	3,414	3,383	45	1,022	2,018
Christiansted NHS	119,335	-	4,422	4,112	62	1,039	2,087
City of Rocks NRES	95,764	-	6,887	6,531	93	2,089	3,815
Clara Barton NHS	15,620	-	1,075	999	11	425	706
*Colonial NHP	3,414,577	-	62,621	57,558	936	22,406	41,049
Colorado NM	435,460	15,188	23,251	21,657	295	6,732	13,242
Congaree NP	120,166	5,503	2,928	2,579	43	1,075	1,942
Coronado NMEM	153,042	-	5,671	5,273	75	1,934	3,552
Cowpens NB	223,923	4	11,854	11,022	176	4,385	7,836
*Crater Lake NP	423,551	79,054	34,688	33,665	549	12,781	24,037
*Craters of the Moon NM	198,545	14,119	6,821	6,746	81	1,748	2,940
Cumberland Gap NHP	828,947	14,887	44,029	40,973	602	10,475	20,889
Cumberland Island NS	74,279	16,961	5,270	5,025	73	2,236	3,959
Curecanti NRA	924,468	53,058	41,288	36,075	450	8,808	18,313
Cuyahoga Valley NP	2,161,185	5,539	51,473	37,248	530	14,931	24,305
*Dayton Aviation Heritage NHP	68,048	-	3,687	3,487	67	1,475	2,638
De Soto NMEM	355,653	-	24,476	22,758	347	11,143	19,676
Death Valley NP	946,867	224,379	50,240	48,087	616	16,114	30,619
Delaware Water Gap NRA	4,986,700	109,067	149,655	127,502	1,998	47,729	93,899
*Denali NP & PRES	406,582	109,047	160,010	160,010	2,669	69,258	111,362

Table A-1. (Continued)

Park Unit	Public Use Data		Visitor Spending 2011		Impacts of Non-local Visitor Spending		
	2011 Recreation Visits	2011 Overnight Stays	All Visitors ($000's)	Non-local Visitors ($000's)	Jobs	Labor Income ($000's)	Value Added ($000's)
Devils Postpile NM	97,207	4,215	3,642	3,394	41	1,028	1,961
Devils Tower NM	395,203	13,313	14,772	13,759	207	4,781	8,075
Dinosaur NM	213,559	40,066	7,671	7,159	92	2,080	3,992
Dry Tortugas NP	75,171	39,318	6,887	6,618	73	2,514	4,261
Edgar Allan Poe NHS	14,711	-	1,012	941	14	505	838
*Effigy Mounds NM	82,581	-	5,124	4,901	82	1,278	2,547
*Eisenhower NHS	58,022	-	3,795	3,763	64	1,218	2,494
El Malpais NM	105,356	417	4,140	3,986	59	1,503	2,594
El Morro NM	48,332	1,943	1,816	1,738	23	365	787
Eleanor Roosevelt NHS	50,074	-	919	567	7	180	361
Eugene O'Neill NHS	2,593	-	178	166	2	89	153
*Everglades NP	934,351	28,868	146,784	141,069	2,336	83,242	140,066
Federal Hall NMEM	187,109	-	12,877	11,973	135	6,193	10,235
Fire Island NS	519,173	37,098	31,692	27,742	309	14,207	23,441
First Ladies NHS	8,254	-	568	528	9	189	341
Flight 93 NMEM	265,246	-	14,042	13,056	193	4,068	7,755
Florissant Fossil Beds NM	61,289	-	3,245	3,017	39	1,062	1,962
Ford's Theatre NHS	642,786	-	21,996	20,096	223	9,163	15,329
*Fort Bowie NHS	8,429	-	968	957	12	266	531
Fort Caroline NMEM	326,149	-	22,446	20,870	325	6,303	11,679

Park Unit	Public Use Data		Visitor Spending 2011		Impacts of Non-local Visitor Spending		
	2011 Recreation Visits	2011 Overnight Stays	All Visitors ($000's)	Non-local Visitors ($000's)	Jobs	Labor Income ($000's)	Value Added ($000's)
Fort Davis NHS	35,130	-	1,302	1,210	17	311	637
Fort Donelson NB	257,389	3	9,538	8,868	132	2,472	4,770
Fort Frederica NM	293,041	-	15,513	14,424	205	5,152	9,558
Fort Laramie NHS	52,916	-	1,961	1,823	27	534	988
*Fort Larned NHS	26,704	-	1,567	1,531	23	449	838
Fort Matanzas NM	570,695	-	39,275	36,518	454	13,063	23,262
Fort McHenry NM & HS	641,254	-	44,131	41,033	586	18,034	32,474
Fort Necessity NB	193,479	577	6,667	5,857	82	1,733	3,241
Fort Point NHS	1,338,508	-	92,117	85,649	1,145	45,382	78,273
Fort Pulaski NM	408,104	26	21,605	20,088	293	8,096	14,199
Fort Raleigh NHS	282,134	-	10,455	9,721	141	3,673	6,645
Fort Scott NHS	26,219	-	972	903	14	237	471
Fort Smith NHS	86,122	-	4,559	4,239	69	1,466	2,643
*Fort Stanwix NM	102,874	-	5,451	5,242	65	1,670	3,755
Fort Sumter NM	857,883	11	21,655	19,312	244	6,261	10,539
Fort Union NM	9,575	-	618	617	8	186	332
Fort Union Trading Post NHS	12,236	-	900	872	11	245	432
Fort Vancouver NHS	710,439	-	37,610	34,969	575	17,117	29,386
Fort Washington Park	409,381	-	14,009	12,799	142	5,836	9,763
Fossil Butte NM	16,552	-	783	783	10	205	397
Franklin Delano Roosevelt MEM	2,309,708	-	79,037	72,209	803	32,925	55,080
Frederick Douglass NHS	46,694	-	1,598	1,460	16	666	1,114
Frederick Law Olmsted NHS	4,022	-	277	257	3	126	209

Table A-1. (Continued)

Park Unit	Public Use Data		Visitor Spending 2011		Impacts of Non-local Visitor Spending		
	2011 Recreation Visits	2011 Overnight Stays	All Visitors ($000's)	Non-local Visitors ($000's)	Jobs	Labor Income ($000's)	Value Added ($000's)
Fredericksburg & Spotsylvania N	908,836	-	48,113	44,735	618	15,068	28,167
Friendship Hill NHS	30,039	-	2,067	1,922	29	634	1,196
Gates of the Arctic NP & PRES	11,623	6,576	4,008	4,008	42	1,343	2,410
Gateway NRA	7,697,727	8,165	150,947	60,712	668	30,724	50,537
Gauley River NRA	109,780	4,765	4,882	4,259	59	1,578	2,570
General Grant NMEM	104,769	-	7,210	6,704	76	3,468	5,731
George Rogers Clark NHP	145,596	-	7,708	7,167	111	1,856	3,676
*George Washington Birthplace NM	130,647	-	3,569	3,275	44	871	1,696
George Washington Carver NM	30,787	-	547	519	7	145	272
George Washington MEM PKWY	7,417,397	-	34,370	5,021	50	1,886	3,084
*Gettysburg NMP	1,124,659	24,948	72,326	71,731	1,226	23,209	47,532
Gila Cliff Dwellings NM	25,317	-	716	690	10	161	312
Glacier Bay NP & PRES	431,986	34,309	4,592	4,592	59	1,765	3,169
Glacier NP	1,853,564	332,491	97,715	93,928	1,337	30,590	55,206
Glen Canyon NRA	2,270,817	1,311,741	233,895	233,895	2,755	88,152	138,044
Golden Gate NRA	14,567,487	60,927	289,700	119,573	1,566	62,428	107,537
*Golden Spike NHS	43,933	-	2,237	2,182	31	709	1,309
Governors Island NM	402,174	-	37,602	35,659	409	18,969	31,399
*Grand Canyon NP	4,298,178	1,357,679	467,257	467,257	7,361	194,112	346,447
Grand Portage NM	97,440	149	11,287	11,228	182	3,445	6,890

Park Unit	Public Use Data		Visitor Spending 2011		Impacts of Non-local Visitor Spending		
	2011 Recreation Visits	2011 Overnight Stays	All Visitors ($000's)	Non-local Visitors ($000's)	Jobs	Labor Income ($000's)	Value Added ($000's)
*Grand Teton NP	2,587,437	483,467	436,416	432,295	6,352	158,759	292,497
Grant-Kohrs Ranch NHS	20,293	-	752	699	11	253	444
Great Basin NP	91,451	36,026	4,528	4,339	56	1,029	2,096
Great Sand Dunes NP & PRES	280,058	46,830	10,770	10,096	134	2,636	5,289
Great Smoky Mountains NP	9,008,830	378,830	818,886	792,559	11,418	293,668	528,578
Greenbelt Park	190,427	24,507	13,539	12,671	134	5,279	8,776
Guadalupe Mountains NP	152,546	14,192	10,919	10,379	158	2,765	5,417
Guilford Courthouse NMP	346,617	12	18,350	17,061	281	7,312	12,746
Gulf Islands NS	5,501,872	138,680	164,709	95,972	1,264	30,575	57,097
Hagerman Fossil Beds NM	21,100	-	678	590	9	191	339
Haleakala NP	956,989	21,436	68,757	65,241	795	26,798	48,229
Hamilton Grange NMEM	7,817	-	533	496	6	266	441
Hampton NHS	32,165	-	2,214	2,058	29	905	1,629
Harpers Ferry NHP	255,348	-	9,993	9,117	135	3,963	6,955
Harry S Truman NHS	28,924	-	1,991	1,851	30	955	1,574
Hawaii Volcanoes NP	1,352,123	80,880	96,990	92,119	1,121	37,711	67,877
Herbert Hoover NHS	134,249	-	7,107	6,608	109	2,513	4,317
Home of Franklin D. Roosevelt NHS	125,488	-	2,723	2,392	29	778	1,577
*Homestead NM of America	69,845	-	2,308	2,161	32	654	1,166
Hopewell Culture NHP	33,834	-	1,254	1,166	18	326	611
Hopewell Furnace NHS	44,873	-	2,376	2,209	33	926	1,615
Horseshoe Bend NMP	65,892	-	3,488	3,243	49	980	1,776
Hot Springs NP	1,396,354	13,943	100,386	95,223	1,551	30,878	54,885

Table A-1. (Continued)

Park Unit	Public Use Data		Visitor Spending 2011		Impacts of Non-local Visitor Spending		
	2011 Recreation Visits	2011 Overnight Stays	All Visitors ($000's)	Non-local Visitors ($000's)	Jobs	Labor Income ($000's)	Value Added ($000's)
Hovenweep NM	25,858	1,558	1,390	1,297	17	403	740
Hubbell Trading Post NHS	88,231	-	4,671	4,343	57	921	2,109
Independence NHP	3,572,770	-	149,894	134,115	1,878	67,770	112,298
Indiana Dunes NL	1,840,513	22,823	58,817	41,251	572	13,892	24,596
Isle Royale NP	15,892	48,787	2,098	2,098	30	524	1,049
*James A. Garfield NHS	31,499	-	1,031	944	15	449	746
Jean Lafitte NHP & PRES	420,366	-	22,254	20,691	292	10,284	16,699
Jefferson NEM	2,259,020	-	97,764	85,939	1,110	44,057	75,918
Jewel Cave NM	77,146	-	4,084	3,797	60	1,319	2,260
Jimmy Carter NHS	66,157	-	2,452	2,279	34	571	1,189
John D. Rockefeller, Jr. MEM PK	1,147,986	34,914	7,471	6,930	93	2,198	3,727
*John Day Fossil Beds NM	148,002	-	7,303	7,185	90	1,668	3,349
John F. Kennedy NHS	18,466	-	1,271	1,182	14	580	962
John Muir NHS	31,236	-	2,150	1,999	26	836	1,557
Johnstown Flood NMEM	105,906	-	6,356	5,870	97	2,161	4,092
*Joshua Tree NP	1,396,237	281,544	50,471	50,031	690	20,220	37,817
Kalaupapa NHP	57,841	-	3,062	2,847	34	1,142	2,049
Kaloko Honokohau NHP	162,906	-	8,624	8,019	96	3,215	5,771
*Katmai NP & PRES	48,939	8,239	12,583	12,445	166	4,928	8,847
Kenai Fjords NP	346,852	1,791	11,804	11,630	159	4,624	8,303

Park Unit	Public Use Data		Visitor Spending 2011		Impacts of Non-local Visitor Spending		
	2011 Recreation Visits	2011 Overnight Stays	All Visitors ($000's)	Non-local Visitors ($000's)	Jobs	Labor Income ($000's)	Value Added ($000's)
Kennesaw Mountain NBP	1,748,436	-	59,809	52,087	644	22,144	36,030
Kings Canyon NP	566,810	182,275	44,116	40,524	549	15,441	29,781
*Kings Mountain NMP	272,325	92	9,992	8,882	135	3,127	5,699
Klondike Gold Rush NHP Alaska	795,150	5,592	22,504	22,236	273	8,226	14,678
Klondike Gold Rush NHP Seattle	64,898	-	4,466	4,153	60	2,025	3,485
Knife River Indian Villages NHS	16,025	-	594	552	9	207	359
Kobuk Valley NP	11,485	9,715	3,955	3,955	41	1,318	2,354
Korean War Veterans Memorial	3,073,430	-	105,171	96,086	1,068	43,812	73,293
Lake Chelan NRA	43,827	10,595	1,803	1,646	23	827	1,414
Lake Clark NP & PRES	5,158	1,931	1,775	1,775	18	590	1,052
Lake Mead NRA	6,396,682	923,421	246,962	209,944	2,544	79,462	138,418
Lake Meredith NRA	734,030	17,098	32,446	28,237	382	8,189	15,636
Lake Roosevelt NRA	1,523,474	162,760	48,758	42,892	563	11,732	22,969
Lassen Volcanic NP	351,269	88,567	15,807	14,403	178	4,458	8,675
Lava Beds NM	124,113	10,827	4,678	4,456	52	1,187	2,319
LBJ Memorial Grove on the Potomc	239,058	-	16,452	15,297	164	6,499	10,807
Lewis & Clark NHP	191,867	-	10,157	9,444	142	2,386	4,794
Lincoln Boyhood NMEM	108,420	-	5,740	5,337	83	1,550	2,906
Lincoln Home NHS	296,214	-	16,367	16,061	233	6,006	11,410
Lincoln Memorial	5,971,220	-	204,331	186,680	2,075	85,120	142,397
Little Bighorn Battlefield NM	312,168	-	11,568	10,756	165	4,036	7,067
Little River Canyon NPRES	225,549	-	11,355	10,768	169	3,237	6,213
Little Rock Central High School NHS	66,106	-	3,500	3,254	52	1,479	2,389

Table A-1. (Continued)

Park Unit	Public Use Data		Visitor Spending 2011		Impacts of Non-local Visitor Spending		
	2011 Recreation Visits	2011 Overnight Stays	All Visitors ($000's)	Non-local Visitors ($000's)	Jobs	Labor Income ($000's)	Value Added ($000's)
Longfellow NHS	46,596	-	2,467	2,294	28	1,126	1,867
Lowell NHP	520,452	-	35,818	33,303	408	16,351	27,109
Lyndon B. Johnson NHP	100,056	-	6,886	6,402	90	2,718	4,738
Maggie L. Walker NHS	10,779	-	271	143	2	66	114
Mammoth Cave NP	483,319	78,172	33,504	31,618	508	11,080	19,822
Manassas NBP	659,740	-	9,669	9,256	105	3,558	5,776
*Manzanar NHS	79,587	-	8,434	8,381	92	2,091	4,286
Marsh-Billings-Rockefeller NHP	29,049	-	1,538	1,430	21	536	932
Martin Luther King Jr. Memorial	1,490,358	-	101,657	94,240	1,017	41,961	70,532
Martin Luther King, Jr. NHS	666,482	-	45,868	42,647	562	21,142	33,915
Martin Van Buren NHS	19,287	-	419	367	4	110	202
Mary McLeod Bethune Council House NHS	18,142	-	621	567	6	259	433
Mesa Verde NP	572,329	70,891	43,382	41,397	551	12,518	24,207
Minute Man NHP	1,002,833	-	69,015	64,170	851	29,855	51,655
*Minuteman Missile NHS	59,389	-	4,229	4,229	65	1,467	2,505
Mississippi NRRA	99,398	-	11,029	10,567	186	5,981	10,155
Missouri NRR	179,983	-	9,061	8,593	140	2,204	4,171
Mojave NPRES	536,006	1,584	12,552	10,978	131	4,624	8,187
*Monocacy NB	36,674	-	2,796	2,591	33	1,299	2,122

Park Unit	Public Use Data		Visitor Spending 2011		Impacts of Non-local Visitor Spending		
	2011 Recreation Visits	2011 Overnight Stays	All Visitors ($000's)	Non-local Visitors ($000's)	Jobs	Labor Income ($000's)	Value Added ($000's)
Montezuma Castle NM	573,731	-	30,373	28,240	428	13,851	24,025
Moores Creek NB	58,118	252	2,150	1,999	31	704	1,293
Morristown NHP	222,395	-	11,773	10,947	123	5,662	9,358
*Mount Rainier NP	1,038,229	162,684	33,006	31,382	436	11,653	21,090
Mount Rushmore NMEM	2,081,722	-	74,365	69,991	1,007	22,080	37,100
Muir Woods NM	897,131	-	61,741	57,406	767	30,417	52,462
Natchez NHP	206,624	-	10,938	10,170	131	2,674	5,243
Natchez Trace PKWY	5,765,343	21,957	93,117	33,926	455	7,618	14,891
National Capital Parks Central	1,240,717	-	42,457	38,789	431	17,686	29,588
National Capital Parks East	1,167,393	-	39,947	36,497	406	16,641	27,839
National Park of American Samoa	8,716	-	744	713	11	188	381
Natural Bridges NM	91,184	6,665	4,918	4,590	59	1,191	2,339
Navajo NM	87,388	2,533	4,655	4,335	56	1,348	2,515
New Bedford Whaling NHP	273,862	-	14,250	13,618	207	6,140	11,616
New Orleans Jazz NHP	130,393	-	6,903	6,418	90	3,190	5,180
*New River Gorge NR	1,071,088	8,861	46,224	43,316	596	13,647	23,667
Nez Perce NHP	286,259	-	10,608	9,863	151	3,849	7,119
Nicodemus NHS	2,681	-	133	130	2	38	68
Ninety Six NHS	70,099	-	3,711	3,450	50	946	1,793
Niobrara NSR	65,785	-	3,312	3,141	51	806	1,525
Noatak NPRES	11,722	9,694	4,036	4,036	42	1,343	2,397
North Cascades NP	19,208	17,002	1,252	1,206	16	582	997
Obed W&SR	212,458	1,340	9,711	8,482	124	2,277	4,420

Table A-1. (Continued)

Park Unit	Public Use Data		Visitor Spending 2011		Impacts of Non-local Visitor Spending		
	2011 Recreation Visits	2011 Overnight Stays	All Visitors ($000's)	Non-local Visitors ($000's)	Jobs	Labor Income ($000's)	Value Added ($000's)
Ocmulgee NM	122,722	-	6,497	6,041	93	2,145	4,109
*Olympic NP	2,966,502	298,235	115,317	105,561	1,497	28,293	59,819
Oregon Caves NM	76,194	6,307	3,848	3,578	55	1,212	2,393
Organ Pipe Cactus NM	211,405	13,024	11,358	10,594	160	5,099	8,869
Ozark NSR	1,365,960	168,595	65,280	57,823	861	13,337	27,211
Padre Island NS	542,873	59,828	38,805	36,897	516	10,304	19,878
Palo Alto Battlefield NHP	24,752	-	917	853	13	303	593
Pea Ridge NMP	114,234	-	6,047	5,623	88	1,537	2,833
Pecos NHP	43,873	-	1,022	989	15	377	642
Pennsylvania Avenue NHS	236,136	-	8,080	7,382	82	3,366	5,631
*Perry's Victory & Intl. Peace M	93,119	1,581	7,422	7,422	147	3,430	6,037
Petersburg NB	213,261	-	11,290	10,497	155	3,799	7,139
Petrified Forest NP	614,054	4,611	44,161	41,879	568	11,735	23,317
Petroglyph NM	114,428	-	5,060	4,098	66	1,728	2,987
*Pictured Rocks NL	561,104	33,974	24,970	24,532	357	5,676	12,414
Pinnacles NM	393,219	-	8,415	6,942	82	2,802	4,823
Pipe Spring NM	57,360	-	3,037	2,823	39	933	1,752
Pipestone NM	61,908	-	2,846	2,762	44	991	1,678
Piscataway Park	279,060	-	9,549	8,724	97	3,978	6,655
Point Reyes NS	2,129,116	40,822	93,317	84,981	1,105	43,524	75,171

Park Unit	Public Use Data		Visitor Spending 2011		Impacts of Non-local Visitor Spending		
	2011 Recreation Visits	2011 Overnight Stays	All Visitors ($000's)	Non-local Visitors ($000's)	Jobs	Labor Income ($000's)	Value Added ($000's)
Port Chicago Naval Magazine NM	545	-	37	34	1	21	36
President W.J. Clinton Birthplace	9,749	-	512	474	7	124	254
President's Park	786,151	-	26,902	24,578	273	11,207	18,748
Prince William Forest Park	379,535	48,504	21,833	16,328	172	6,494	10,808
Pu'uhonua o Honaunau NHP	426,224	-	22,564	20,980	252	8,412	15,099
Pu'ukohola Heiau NHS	133,306	-	7,057	6,562	79	2,631	4,722
Rainbow Bridge NM	92,311	-	4,887	4,544	60	1,485	2,701
Redwood NP	380,167	5,420	20,172	18,186	247	4,689	9,966
Richmond NBP	139,376	-	10,374	9,335	146	4,420	7,697
Rio Grande W&SR	873	4,871	106	105	1	22	45
River Raisin NBP	36,206	-	3,090	2,961	52	1,667	2,837
Rock Creek Park	2,050,490	-	70,166	64,105	713	29,230	48,899
Rocky Mountain NP	3,176,941	200,712	196,127	191,892	2,742	71,849	138,269
Roger Williams NMEM	50,909	-	3,504	3,258	46	1,420	2,459
Ross Lake NRA	728,353	71,820	23,339	20,516	280	9,832	16,804
Russell Cave NM	20,717	-	1,097	1,020	16	274	526
Sagamore Hill NHS	53,336	-	3,671	3,413	41	1,516	2,726
Saguaro NP	610,045	2,033	21,949	15,156	211	5,547	10,044
Saint Croix NSR	273,729	29,738	8,803	7,740	122	2,348	4,293
Saint Paul's Church NHS	14,926	-	1,027	955	11	494	816
*Saint-Gaudens NHS	32,695	-	1,297	1,193	19	494	869
Salem Maritime NHS	737,073	-	50,726	47,164	578	23,157	38,392
Salinas Pueblo Missions NM	29,786	-	823	792	12	306	520

Table A-1. (Continued)

Park Unit	Public Use Data		Visitor Spending 2011		Impacts of Non-local Visitor Spending		
	2011 Recreation Visits	2011 Overnight Stays	All Visitors ($000's)	Non-local Visitors ($000's)	Jobs	Labor Income ($000's)	Value Added ($000's)
Salt River Bay NHP & Ecological	2,419	-	206	198	3	52	106
San Antonio Missions NHP	568,021	-	23,831	21,323	297	8,913	15,385
San Francisco Maritime NHP	4,224,897	10,876	95,492	70,774	855	33,761	58,207
San Juan Island NHP	266,717	-	18,356	17,067	235	5,939	11,420
San Juan NHS	1,229,590	-	65,093	60,523	892	17,812	34,157
Sand Creek Massacre NHS	3,935	-	336	322	4	80	172
Santa Monica Mountains NRA	609,636	144	26,192	17,258	242	9,013	15,833
Saratoga NHP	65,043	-	2,410	2,241	27	700	1,426
Saugus Iron Works NHS	11,121	-	765	712	9	349	579
Scotts Bluff NM	128,811	-	4,416	3,586	60	1,134	2,033
*Sequoia NP	1,006,583	228,644	77,776	71,141	965	27,119	52,409
Shenandoah NP	1,209,883	282,888	73,908	65,113	938	22,465	41,855
Shiloh NMP	387,816	-	14,371	13,362	202	4,033	7,844
Sitka NHP	186,864	-	4,058	4,010	49	1,483	2,645
*Sleeping Bear Dunes NL	1,348,304	129,973	132,774	129,244	2,288	52,893	102,846
Springfield Armory NHS	16,161	-	1,112	1,034	14	438	800
Statue of Liberty NM	3,749,982	-	174,607	157,217	2,009	79,828	137,508
Steamtown NHS	111,725	-	4,140	3,850	59	1,529	2,759
Stones River NB	187,208	-	9,911	9,215	143	4,716	7,784
Sunset Crater Volcano NM	185,265	-	9,808	9,119	121	2,986	5,514

Park Unit	Public Use Data		Visitor Spending 2011		Impacts of Non-local Visitor Spending		
	2011 Recreation Visits	2011 Overnight Stays	All Visitors ($000's)	Non-local Visitors ($000's)	Jobs	Labor Income ($000's)	Value Added ($000's)
Tallgrass Prairie NPRES	17,893	-	901	854	14	225	433
Thaddeus Kosciuszko NMEM	1,949	-	134	125	2	67	111
Theodore Roosevelt Birthplace NHS	6,537	-	450	418	5	216	358
Theodore Roosevelt Inaugural NHS	17,107	-	1,177	1,095	15	416	840
Theodore Roosevelt Island Park	137,690	-	9,476	8,811	95	3,743	6,225
Theodore Roosevelt NP	563,407	21,518	28,318	26,881	431	8,784	15,313
Thomas Edison NHP	55,284	-	3,805	3,538	40	1,830	3,024
Thomas Jefferson MEM	1,945,696	-	66,580	60,829	676	27,736	46,400
Thomas Stone NHS	6,351	-	437	406	4	173	287
Timpanogos Cave NM	96,965	-	6,673	6,205	100	2,856	4,840
Timucuan EHP	1,028,922	-	56,265	43,836	617	19,121	33,487
Tonto NM	53,426	-	2,828	2,630	40	1,279	2,227
Tumacacori NHP	33,740	-	1,250	1,163	16	426	783
Tuskegee Airmen NHS	16,244	-	860	800	13	303	523
Tuskegee Institute NHS	23,288	-	1,233	1,146	18	435	749
Tuzigoot NM	101,104	-	5,352	4,977	75	2,441	4,234
Ulysses S. Grant NHS	35,664	-	2,454	2,282	31	1,209	2,086
Upper Delaware S&RR	270,390	-	8,636	7,538	89	2,182	4,207
*Valley Forge NHP	1,303,046	2,000	49,497	35,127	560	21,595	34,786
Vanderbilt Mansion NHS	367,680	-	5,761	3,363	39	1,025	2,023
Vicksburg NMP	796,035	-	42,141	39,182	589	16,080	27,139
Vietnam Veterans MEM	4,020,127	-	137,566	125,682	1,397	57,307	95,869
*Virgin Islands NP	442,414	57,741	58,649	58,649	1,086	21,565	40,139

Table A-1. (Continued)

Park Unit	Public Use Data		Visitor Spending 2011		Impacts of Non-local Visitor Spending		
	2011 Recreation Visits	2011 Overnight Stays	All Visitors ($000's)	Non-local Visitors ($000's)	Jobs	Labor Income ($000's)	Value Added ($000's)
Voyageurs NP	177,184	65,465	8,972	8,593	137	2,993	5,566
Walnut Canyon NM	125,003	-	6,618	6,153	82	2,015	3,721
War in the Pacific NHP	482,391	-	17,876	16,621	245	4,892	9,380
Washington Monument	430,153	-	14,720	13,448	150	6,132	10,258
Washita Battlefield NHS	10,995	-	456	428	7	110	222
Weir Farm NHS	22,415	-	1,543	1,434	16	692	1,161
Whiskeytown NRA	761,710	43,713	33,980	29,683	386	8,906	18,157
White House	570,057	-	19,507	17,822	198	8,126	13,594
White Sands NM	428,924	2,185	15,812	15,500	230	5,053	9,091
Whitman Mission NHS	57,611	-	2,135	1,985	28	601	1,143
William Howard Taft NHS	21,141	-	1,455	1,353	22	646	1,053
Wilson's Creek NB	192,865	-	10,210	9,493	156	3,689	6,705
Wind Cave NP	538,394	3,054	51,506	51,381	890	19,661	34,288
Wolf Trap NP for the Performing Arts	425,177	-	29,261	27,206	292	11,558	19,222
*Women's Rights NHP	25,426	-	740	740	7	173	334
World War II Memorial	3,752,172	-	128,397	117,305	1,304	53,487	89,479
World War II Valor in the Pacific NM	1,694,896	-	71,109	63,623	735	24,117	42,948
Wrangell-St. Elias NP & PRES	65,225	-	3,110	3,110	44	1,174	2,123
Wright Brothers NMEM	445,455	-	16,507	15,348	223	5,800	10,491
Wupatki NM	216,165	-	11,444	10,640	141	3,484	6,434

Park Unit	Public Use Data		Visitor Spending 2011		Impacts of Non-local Visitor Spending		
	2011 Recreation Visits	2011 Overnight Stays	All Visitors ($000's)	Non-local Visitors ($000's)	Jobs	Labor Income ($000's)	Value Added ($000's)
*Yellowstone NP	3,394,326	1,280,978	332,975	332,975	5,041	133,534	227,947
*Yosemite NP	3,951,393	1,630,610	379,116	374,136	5,003	128,202	251,573
Yukon-Charley Rivers NPRES	1,718	6,774	1,966	1,966	21	670	1,217
*Zion NP	2,825,505	312,608	138,697	137,403	2,286	51,416	98,433

For these parks, results are based on a visitor survey at the designated park. For other parks, visitor characteristics and spending averages are adapted from national averages for each park type, adjusted for surrounding populations and spending opportunities.

Notes: Non-local visitors live outside a roughly 60-mile radius of the park. Jobs include part-time and full-time jobs with seasonal jobs adjusted to an annual basis. Impacts include direct and secondary effects of visitor spending on the local economy. Labor income covers wages and salaries, payroll benefits, and incomes of sole proprietors in the local region. Value added includes labor income, profits and rents, and indirect business taxes.

Table A-2. State-Level Impacts of NPS Visitor Spending on State Economies by State, 2011

State	Non-local Visitor Spending ($ Millions)	Jobs from Non-local Visitor Spending	Labor Income from Non-local Visitor Spending ($ Millions)	Value-added from Nonlocal Visitor Spending ($ Millions)
Alaska	237	4,138	116	200
Alabama	19	315	8	13
Arkansas	140	2,364	53	92
American Samoa	1	12	0[a]	1
Arizona	737	12,499	381	671
California	1,192	17,978	690	1,224
Colorado	319	4,621	148	266
Connecticut	1	19	1	1
District of Columbia	1,025	8,852	404	684
Florida	608	9,818	320	561
Georgia	241	3,592	108	189
Guam	17	268	8	14
Hawaii	259	3,113	104	187
Iowa	12	195	5	8
Idaho	24	379	8	15
Illinois	16	253	9	16
Indiana	54	826	20	35
Kansas	4	67	2	3
Kentucky	85	1,400	36	62
Louisiana	28	429	12	21
Massachusetts	432	6,917	179	307
Maryland	145	2,025	65	115
Maine	183	2,555	97	169
Michigan	159	2,875	82	148
Minnesota	37	665	19	33
Missouri	158	2,468	67	116
Mississippi	101	1,471	35	61
Montana	279	4,492	107	190
North Carolina	725	11,915	323	560
North Dakota	28	478	11	18
Nebraska	13	227	5	9
New Hampshire	1	20	1	1
New Jersey	117	1,807	63	113
New Mexico	98	1,479	36	63
Nevada	162	2,045	67	116

State	Non-local Visitor Spending ($ Millions)	Jobs from Non-local Visitor Spending	Labor Income from Non-local Visitor Spending ($ Millions)	Value-added from Nonlocal Visitor Spending ($ Millions)
New York	341	3,998	159	274
Ohio	52	862	22	39
Oklahoma	14	177	5	9
Oregon	54	915	26	45
Pennsylvania	325	5,358	161	280
Puerto Rico	61	980	29	50
Rhode Island	3	45	1	2
South Carolina	48	704	18	31
South Dakota	160	2,576	54	93
Tennessee	530	8,847	261	452
Texas	177	2,798	91	164
Utah	693	11,240	336	565
Virginia	541	8,116	237	417
Virgin Islands	65	1,236	37	63
Vermont	1	22	1	1
Washington	261	3,827	121	215
Wisconsin	24	455	12	19
West Virginia	60	869	21	36
Wyoming	621	9,098	222	397

[a] $0.35 million for labor income.

Table A-3. Regional-Level Impacts of NPS Visitor Spending on Regional Economies by Region, 2011

Region	Non-local Visitor Spending ($ Millions)	Jobs from Non-local Visitor Spending	Labor Income from Non- local Visitor Spending ($ Millions)	Value-added from Nonlocal Visitor Spending ($ Millions)
Alaska Region	237	4,138	116	200
Intermountain Region	2,885	48,326	1,569	2,811
Midwest Region	854	15,630	462	810
National Capital Region	1,209	15,225	587	984
Northeast Region	1,847	28,802	1,071	1,873
Pacific West Region	2,022	30,612	1,144	2,026
Southeast Region	2,631	44,944	1,397	2,461

Table A-4. Allocations to States for Multi-State Parks

Park	State	Share
Assateague Island NS	MD	33%
Assateague Island NS	VA	67%
Bighorn Canyon NRA	WY	46%
Bighorn Canyon NRA	MT	54%
Big South Fork NRRA	KY	41%
Big South Fork NRRA	TN	59%
Blue Ridge Parkway	VA	38%
Blue Ridge Parkway	NC	62%
Chickamauga & Chattanooga NMP	GA	50%
Chickamauga & Chattanooga NMP	TN	50%
Chesapeake & Ohio Canal NHP	WV	6%
Chesapeake & Ohio Canal NHP	MD	9%
Chesapeake & Ohio Canal NHP	DC	85%
Cumberland Gap NHP	KY	93%
Cumberland Gap NHP	VA	7%
Delaware Water Gap NRA	PA	29%
Delaware Water Gap NRA	NJ	71%
Dinosaur NM	UT	26%
Dinosaur NM	CO	74%
Gateway NRA	NJ	20%
Gateway NRA	NY	80%
Glen Canyon NRA	AZ	8%
Glen Canyon NRA	UT	92%
Great Smoky Mountains NP	NC	44%
Great Smoky Mountains NP	TN	56%
Gulf Islands Nat Seashore	MS	25%
Gulf Islands Nat Seashore	FL	75%
Hovenweep NM	CO	44%
Hovenweep NM	UT	56%
Lake Mead NRA	AZ	25%
Lake Mead NRA	NV	75%
Natchez Trace Parkway	AL	7%
Natchez Trace Parkway	TN	13%
Natchez Trace Parkway	MS	80%
National capital Parks East	MD	10%
National capital Parks East	DC	90%
Saint Croix Nat scenic river	MN	50%
Saint Croix Nat scenic river	WI	50%
Upper Delaware SRR	NY	50%
Upper Delaware SRR	PA	50%
Yellowstone NP	WY	49%
Yellowstone NP	MT	51%

End Notes

[1] National estimates use multipliers for the U.S. economy.

[2] The 60-mile radius is a general average representing the primary impact region around most parks. The radius is closer to 30 miles for parks in urban settings, and as large as 100 miles for some western parks. Economic multipliers are based on regions defined as groupings of counties to approximate a 60-mile radius of the park.

[3] These studies are conducted by the Visitor Services Project (VSP) at the University of Idaho. Reports for individual parks are available at their website: http://www.psu.uidaho.edu/vsp.reports.htm

[4] For example, spending during extended stays in an area while visiting relatives, on business, or when the park visit was not the primary trip purpose is excluded. For most historic sites and parks in urban areas, spending for one day or night is counted for each park entry. Where several park units are within a 60-mile radius, adjustments are made for those visiting more than one park on the same day.

[5] Day trips include pass-thru visitors not spending a night within 60 miles of the park, as well as stays with friends and relatives and in owned seasonal homes.

[6] Spending figures exclude airfares and other trip spending beyond 60 miles of the park. Purchases of durable goods (boats, RVs) and major equipment are also excluded. Special expenses for commercial rafting trips, air overflights and other special activities are not fully captured for all parks.

[7] Secondary effects include indirect effects of businesses buying goods and services from backward-linked local firms and induced effects of household spending of their earnings.

[8] To the extent possible, spending not directly associated with a park visit is also excluded. For example, only one night's expenses are counted for visitors in the area primarily on business, visiting relatives, or visiting other attractions. For parks with visitor surveys, spending attributed to a park visit was estimated based on the percentage of visitors identifying the park visit as the primary purpose of the trip.

[9] Local economic ratios are therefore used to estimate the direct effects. National multipliers are used to estimate secondary effects. With the exception of wholesale trade and manufacturing sectors, the national direct effects (Table 5) are therefore the same as the local direct effects (Table 3).

[10] Visits are classified as day trips by local visitors, day trips by non-local visitors, and overnight trips by visitors staying in campgrounds or hotels, lodges, cabins, and bed and breakfasts. For parks with lodging facilities within the park, visitors staying in park lodges, campgrounds, or back-country sites are distinguished from those staying outside the park in motels or non-NPS campgrounds. Visitors staying with friends or relatives, in owned seasonal homes, or passing through without a local overnight stay are generally treated as day trips.

[11] Detailed impact reports for parks that have included economic questions in their VSP studies are available at the MGM2 (http://mgm2impact.com/) or NPS social science websites (http://www.nature.nps.gov/socialscience/products.cfm# MGM2Reports).

In: Economic Contributions of National Park ... ISBN: 978-1-60876-005-3
Editor: Jenell Meehan

Chapter 3

ECONOMIC BENEFITS TO LOCAL COMMUNITIES FROM NATIONAL PARK VISITATION AND PAYROLL, 2010*

Daniel J. Stynes

EXECUTIVE SUMMARY

The National Park System received 281 million recreation visits in 2010. Park visitors spent $12.13 billion in local gateway regions (within roughly 60 miles of the park). Visitors staying outside the park in motels, hotels, cabins and bed and breakfasts accounted for 56% of the total spending. Half of the spending was for lodging and meals, 19% for gas and local transportation, 10% for amusements, 8% for groceries, and 13% for other retail purchases.

The contribution of this spending to the national economy is 258,400 jobs, $9.8 billion in labor income, and $16.6 billion in value added[1]. The direct effects of visitor spending are at the local level in gateway regions around national parks. Local economic impacts were estimated after excluding spending by visitors from the local area (9.8% of the total). Combining local impacts across all parks yields a total local impact including direct and secondary effects of 156,280 jobs, $4.68 billion in labor income, and $7.65 billion value added. The four local economic sectors most directly affected by

---

* This is an edited, reformatted and augmented version of Natural Resource Report NPS/NRSS/EQD/NRR—2011/481, issued by the National Park Service, December 2011.

non-local visitor spending are lodging, restaurants, retail trade, and amusements. Visitor spending supports 43,160 jobs in restaurants and bars, 32,000 jobs in lodging sectors, 23,000 jobs in retail and wholesale trade, and 18,560 jobs in amusements.

Parks also impact the local and national economies through the NPS payroll. In Fiscal Year 2010 the National Park Service employed 26,031 people with a total payroll of $1,709 million in wages, salaries, and payroll benefits. Including the induced effects of the spending of NPS wages and salaries in the local region, the total local economic impacts of park payrolls are $1.95 billion in labor income, $2.16 billion in value added, and 32,407 jobs (including NPS jobs). The impacts of the park payroll on the national economy are $2.41 billion in labor income, $2.96 billion in value added, and 41,700 jobs Combining the impacts of non-local visitor spending and NPS payroll-related spending yields a total impact of 300,000 jobs nationally of which 189,000 are in the local regions around national parks.

INTRODUCTION

This report provides updated estimates of National Park Service (NPS) visitor spending for 2010 and estimates the economic impacts of visitor spending and the NPS payroll on local economies. Visitor spending and impacts are estimated using the Money Generation Model version 2 (MGM2) model (Stynes et al., 2000) based on calendar year 2010 park visits, spending averages from park visitor surveys, and local area economic multipliers. Impacts of the NPS payroll are estimated based on fiscal year (FY) 2010 payroll data for each park.

Visitor spending impacts are estimated for all park units with visitation data. Payroll impacts are estimated for all parks including administrative units and parks without visit count data. Impacts measure the direct and secondary effects of visitor spending and park payrolls in terms of jobs, income, and value added.[2] Direct effects cover businesses selling goods and services directly to park visitors. Secondary effects include indirect effects resulting from sales to backward-linked industries within the local region and induced effects from household spending of income earned directly or indirectly from visitor spending. Impacts of construction activity and park purchases of goods and services are not included.

Impacts are estimated at both the national and local level. Most spending directly associated with park visits occurs in gateway regions around each park. Impacts of this spending on the local economies are estimated using local input-output models for each park. Local regions are defined as a 60-mile radius[3] around each park. To estimate impacts on the national economy, spending within roughly 60 miles of the park is applied to the national input-output model. System-wide totals covering impacts on local economies are also estimated by summing the spending and local impact estimates for all park units. Results for individual park units are reported in the Appendix.

2010 Updates

The 2010 estimates reflect new visitor surveys at seven parks. In 2010 visitor surveys were conducted at Delaware Water Gap NRA, Fort Union NM, Fossil Butte NM, George Washington Carver NM, New Bedford Whaling NHP, Rocky Mt. NP, and Wind Cave NP .[4] Spending and visitor profiles for these parks were updated based upon the survey data. For other parks, spending profiles from 2009 were price adjusted to 2010 using Bureau of Labor Statistics consumer price indices for each spending category. Consumer prices remained fairly stable between 2009 and 2010 except for an increase of 18% in gas prices and an 8% increase in transportation costs.

Visitor segment mixes were assumed to be unchanged except as reflected in overnight stays or new visitor surveys. Except for parks with new visitor surveys, average party sizes, lengths of stay and re-entry factors were assumed to be unchanged from 2009. Visit and overnight stay figures for all parks were updated to 2010 from the NPS public use statistics (Street 2011).

Multipliers for individual parks were estimated last year based on 2008 IMPLAN data and IMPLAN's trade flow models (Stynes, 2010). Local regions were defined to include all counties within roughly 60 road miles of each park. For 2010, local region multipliers were adjusted from 2008 to 2009 based on structural changes in the national economy (i.e., ratios of jobs, income and value added to sales in each sector). Secondary effects and direct job ratios were adjusted to 2010 based on consumer price indices.

Recreation Visits

The National Park System received 281.3 million recreation visits in 2010. Visitor spending was estimated by dividing visitors to each park into segments with distinct spending patterns and applying spending averages based on surveys of park visitors at selected parks. As spending averages are measured on a party day basis (party nights for overnight trips), the NPS counts of recreation visits are converted from person entries to a park to party days in the area by applying average party size, length of stay, and park re-entry factors. This adjusts for some double counting of visits. To the extent possible, spending not directly related to a park visit is excluded.[5]

In 2010 there were 14.58 million recreation overnight stays in the parks, representing 3.3% of all visits. Twenty-nine percent of park visits were day trips by local residents, 40% were day trips from 60 miles or more,[6] and 31% involved an overnight stay near the park. Visitor spending depends on the number of days spent in the local area and also the type of lodging on overnight trips. Non-local day trips account for 34% of the party days spent in the local area, local day trips 28%, and overnight stays 38%. Sixty-four percent of all overnight stays by park visitors are in motels, lodges, or bed and breakfasts outside the park; another 18% are in campgrounds outside the park, 6% in private homes; and 12% are inside the park in NPS campgrounds, lodges, or backcountry sites.

VISITOR SPENDING

Visitor spending averages cover expenses within the local region, excluding park entry fees. Spending averages for each segment are derived from park visitor surveys at selected parks over the past ten years. Bureau of Labor Statistics price indices for each spending category are applied to adjust all spending to 2010 dollars.

NPS System-wide spending averages for 2010 are given in Table 1 for seven distinct visitor segments. A typical park visitor party on a day trip spends $40 if a local resident and $70 if non-local (Table 1).

On a party night basis, spending by visitors on overnight trips varies from $47 for backcountry campers to $341 for visitors staying in park lodges. Campers spend $116 per night if staying outside the park and $101 if staying inside the park. Spending averages at individual parks vary from these system-wide averages due to differences in local prices and spending opportunities. For example, while non-local visitors on day trips spent $39 per party at Badlands NP in 2010, their counterparts at Grand Canyon spent $146.

In total, park visitors spent $12.13 billion in the local region surrounding the parks in 2010.[7] Local residents account for 9.8% of this spending (Table

2). Visitors staying in motels and lodges outside the park account for 56% of the total spending while non-local visitors on day trips contribute 20% of all spending.

Lodging and restaurant/bar expenses each account for about a quarter of the spending. Transportation expenses (mainly auto fuel) account for 19%, groceries 8%, other retail purchases 13%, and recreation and entertainment 10% (Figure 1).

Table 1. National Park Visitor Spending in the Local Area by Segment, 2010 ($ per party per day/night)

	Visitor Segment						
Spending category	Local Day Trip	Non-local Day Trip	NPS Lodge	NPS Camp Ground	Back-country	Motel-Outside Park	Camp-Outside Park
Motel, hotel, B&B	0.00	0.02	157.57	0.83	3.02	104.82	0.16
Camping fees	0.00	0.00	1.24	18.09	1.99	0.24	25.33
Restaurants & bars	12.61	19.37	73.42	13.86	7.35	62.45	16.56
Amusements	4.56	9.25	29.11	9.99	5.75	20.62	15.21
Groceries	6.08	6.86	14.06	16.32	5.71	15.29	12.63
Gas & oil	8.75	18.97	22.27	24.59	12.73	22.60	23.82
Local transportation	0.55	1.97	14.11	4.42	1.20	9.19	2.12
Retail Purchases	7.80	13.16	28.78	13.27	8.94	27.21	19.69
Total	40.36	69.60	340.55	101.39	46.69	262.41	115.51

Note: Columns may not sum to totals due to rounding.

Table 2. National Park Visitor Spending by Segment, 2010

Segment	Total Spending ($ Millions)	Percent of Spending
Local Day Trip	1,186	9.8%
Non-local Day Trip	2,448	20.2%
Lodge/Cabin-In Park	375	3.1%
Camp-In Park	294	2.4%
Backcountry Campers	32	0.3%
Motel-Outside Park	6,742	55.6%
Camp-Outside Park	815	6.7%
Other Overnight Visitors	242	2.0%
Total	12,134	100.0%

[a] Other overnight visitors include visitors staying overnight in the area but not incurring lodging costs.

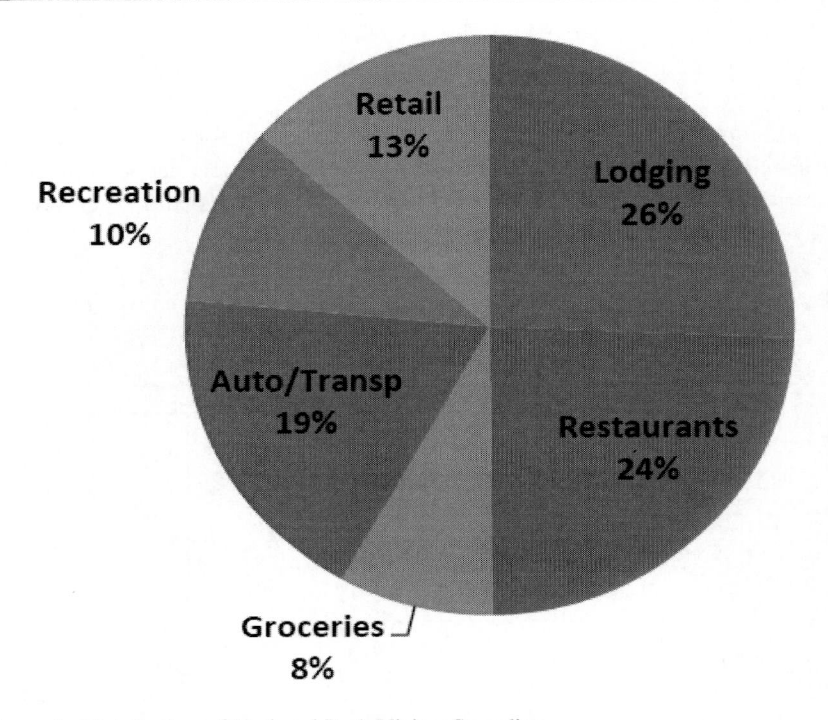

Figure 1. Distribution of National Park Visitor Spending.

LOCAL IMPACTS OF VISITOR SPENDING

Local economic impacts of visitor spending are estimated in the MGM2 model using multipliers for local areas around each park. Multipliers capture both the direct and secondary economic effects in gateway communities around the parks in terms of jobs, labor income, and value added. National totals are calculated as the sum of the local impacts for 356 park units that have counts of visitors.

Both economic significance and economic impacts were estimated. The economic significance estimates in Table 3 measure the impacts of all visitor spending ($12.13 billion), including that of local visitors. Economic impacts in Table 4 exclude spending by local visitors, estimating the impacts of the $10.95 billion spent by visitors who do not reside within the local region.

Table 3. Economic Significance of National Park Visitor Spending to Local Economies, 2010

Sector/Spending category	Sales ($ Millions)	Jobs	Labor Income ($ Millions)	Value Added ($ Millions)
Direct Effects				
Motel, hotel cabin or B&B	2,879	28,980	898	1,600
Camping fees	241	2,966	88	123
Restaurants & bars	2,931	49,136	1,110	1,563
Amusements & Entertain.	1,215	20,804	519	795
Other vehicle expenses	139	1,987	74	89
Local transportation	283	6,240	141	177
Grocery stores	253	4,395	132	214
Gas stations	405	5,875	207	338
Other retail	783	14,936	409	665
Wholesale Trade	291	1,569	111	191
Local Manufacturing.	266	460	27	54
Total Direct Effects	**9,686**	**137,348**	**3,715**	**5,808**
Secondary Effects	4,615	34,505	1,475	2,660
Total Effects	**14,301**	**171,853**	**5,190**	**8,468**

Notes: Economic significance covers all $12.13 billion in spending of park visitors in the local region, including that of local visitors. Jobs include full-time and part-time jobs with seasonal positions adjusted to an annual basis. Labor income covers wages and salaries, including income of sole proprietors and payroll benefits. Value added is the sum of labor income, profits and rents, and indirect business taxes. Columns may not sum to totals due to rounding.

Table 4. Economic Impacts of National Park Visitor Spending on Local Economies, 2010

Sector/Spending category	Sales ($ Millions)	Jobs	Labor Income ($ Millions)	Value Added ($ Millions)
Direct Effects				
Motel, hotel cabin or B&B	2,879	28,980	898	1,600
Camping fees	241	2,966	88	123
Restaurants & bars	2,560	43,160	966	1,362
Amusements & Entertain.	1,081	18,559	461	705
Other vehicle expenses	125	1,804	66	80
Local transportation	280	6,174	140	175
Grocery stores	208	3,652	108	175
Gas stations	348	5,104	177	290
Other retail	673	12,892	352	572

Table 4. (Continued)

Sector/Spending category	Sales ($ Millions)	Jobs	Labor Income ($ Millions)	Value Added ($ Millions)
Wholesale Trade	240	1,320	91	157
Local Manufacturing	200	351	20	40
Total Direct Effects	**8,836**	**124,962**	**3,367**	**5,279**
Secondary Effects	4,122	31,317	1,316	2,371
Total Effects	**12,958**	**156,279**	**4,683**	**7,650**

Note: Economic impacts cover the $10.95 billion spent by non-local visitors. Columns may not sum to totals due to rounding.

Economic impact measures attempt to estimate the likely losses in economic activity to the region in the absence of the park. Should the park opportunities not be available, it is assumed that local residents would spend the money on other local activities, while visitors from outside the region would not have made a trip to the region.[8] Spending by local residents on visits to the park do not represent —new money|| to the region and are therefore generally excluded when estimating impacts. Local resident spending is included in the economic significance measures, as these capture all economic activity associated with park visits, including local and non-local visitors.

Economic Significance

The $12.13 billion spent by park visitors within 60 miles of the park (Table 2) has a total economic effect (significance) of $14.30 billion in sales, $5.19 billion in labor income, and $8.47 billion in value added. Visitor spending supports about 171,850 jobs in gateway regions. Total effects may be divided between the direct effects that occur in businesses selling goods and services directly to park visitors and secondary effects that result from the circulation of this money within the local economy.[9]

Direct effects are $9.68 billion in sales, $3.71 billion in labor income, $5.81 billion in value added, and 137,350 jobs. The local region captures 80% of all visitor spending as direct sales. Note that direct sales of $9.68 billion is less than the $12.13 billion in visitor spending as most of the manufacturing share of retail purchases (groceries, gas, sporting goods, souvenirs) is not included. It is assumed that most of the producer price of retail purchases immediately leaks out of the region to cover the cost of goods sold. Sales figures for retail and wholesale trade are the margins on retail purchases.

The average sales multiplier across all local park regions is 1.47. For every dollar of direct sales another $ .47 in sales is generated in the local region through secondary effects.

Economic Impacts

Excluding $1.19 billion dollars spent by local residents on park visits reduces the total spending to $10.95 billion (Table 2) for the impact analysis. Local visitors represent about 29% of all visits but less than 10% of all visitor spending. The total effects of visitor spending excluding locals is $12.96 billion in sales, $4.68 billion in labor income, $7.65 billion in value added, and 156,280 jobs. The economic sectors most directly affected are lodging, restaurants, retail trade, and amusements. Non-local visitor spending supports 43,160 jobs in restaurants and bars, 32,000 jobs in lodging sectors, 23,000 jobs in retail and wholesale trade, and 18,560 jobs in amusements.

National Economic Significance of NPS Visitor Spending

The contribution of NPS visitor spending to the national economy can be estimated by applying the spending totals to multipliers for the national economy. This circulates spending that occurs within gateway regions around national parks within the broader national economy, capturing impacts on sectors that manufacture goods purchased by park visitors and additional secondary effects.

The estimates do not include spending by park visitors at home for durable goods such as camping, hunting and fishing equipment, recreation vehicles, boats, and other goods used on trips to the national parks. The estimates also exclude airfares and other en route spending that occurs more than 60 miles from the park. Since many long-distance trips involve multiple purposes and often visits to multiple parks, it is difficult to capture these expenses without double counting or attributing spending not directly related to a national park visit.

With the above exclusions, the contribution of visitor spending to the national economy is 258,400 jobs, $9.81 billion in labor income, and $16.62 billion in value added (Table 5). With the exception of manufacturing activity and a portion of activity in wholesale trade, the direct effects of visitor spending accrue to local regions around national parks.[10]

Compared to the contribution to local economies (Table 4), an additional 88,200 jobs are supported nationally by NPS visitor spending, primarily due to the greater indirect and induced effects at the national level. The sales multiplier for NPS visitor spending at the national level is 2.65, compared to an average of 1.46 for local regions around national parks.

Table 5. Economic Significance of National Park Visitor Spending on National Economy, 2010

Sector/Spending category	Sales ($ Millions)	Jobs	Labor Income ($ Millions)	Value Added ($ Millions)
Direct Effects				
Motel, hotel, cabin or B&B	2,879	29,253	909	1,588
Camping fees	241	2,949	93	127
Restaurants & bars	2,929	47,007	1,071	1,508
Amusements & Entertain.	1,214	21,323	534	810
Other vehicle expenses	139	1,901	71	86
Local transportation	283	6,217	141	177
Grocery stores	253	4,247	129	209
Gas stations	405	6,443	208	333
Other retail	783	14,432	402	658
Wholesale Trade	472	2,344	180	310
Local Manufacturing	2,137	3,609	222	506
Total Direct Effects	11,734	139,725	3,961	6,313
Secondary Effects	19,346	118,691	5,851	10,310
Total Effects	31,080	258,416	9,812	16,623

IMPACTS OF NPS PAYROLLS

National park units also impact local and national economies through their own spending, especially NPS payrolls. Payroll impacts were estimated for FY 2010. In FY 2010 the National Park Service employed 26,031 people[11] with a total payroll of $1,709 million in wages, salaries, and payroll benefits (Table

6). Including the induced effects of the spending of NPS wages and salaries in the local region, the total local economic impact of park payrolls on local economies in 2010 was $1.95 billion in labor income, $2.16 billion in value added, and 32,407 jobs. Impacts on the U.S. economy were $2.41 billion in labor income, $2.96 billion in value added and 41,689 jobs.

Table 6. NPS Payroll Impacts on Local and National Economies, 2010

	Jobs	Labor Income ($Millions)	Value Added ($Millions)
NPS Payroll	26,031	1,709	1,709
Local Impacts			
Induced effects	6,376	242	456
Total Local Impacts	32,407	1,950	2,164
National Impacts			
Induced Effects	15,658	704	1,250
Total National Impacts	41,689	2,413	2,959

Note: Columns may not sum to totals due to rounding.

Impacts of park payrolls for each park unit were estimated by applying economic multipliers to wage and salary data to capture the induced effects of NPS employee spending on local economies. The overall local employment multiplier for NPS jobs is 1.25. For every four NPS jobs, another local job is supported through the induced effects of employee spending in the local region. The national employment multiplier is 1.60, due to a greater number of secondary jobs when we allow spending to circulate beyond the local region. There are additional local and national economic effects from NPS purchases of goods and services and from construction activity. These impacts were not estimated.

The visitor spending and payroll impacts may be combined, as park admission fees and most other visitor spending accruing to the National Park Service were omitted from the visitor spending figures to avoid double counting.[12] Using the visitor spending impact estimates from Table 4, which exclude spending of local visitors, the combined total impacts including secondary effects are $6.63 billion in labor income, $9.81 billion in value added, and 188,686 local jobs. Visitor spending accounts for 83% of the total jobs and 78% of the total value added (Table 7).

Table 7. Combined Impacts on Local Economies –Visitor Spending and Payroll

Impact Measure	Visitor Spending Impacts[a]	NPS Payroll Impacts	Combined Impacts	Visitor Spending Share
Direct Effects				
Jobs	124,962	26,031	150,993	83%
Labor Income ($ Millions)	3,367	1,709	5,076	66%
Value Added ($ Millions)	5,279	1,709	6,988	76%
Total Effects				
Jobs	156,279	32,407	188,686	83%
Labor Income ($ Millions)	4,683	1,950	6,634	71%
Value Added ($ Millions)	7,650	2,164	9,815	78%

[a] Excludes spending by local visitors

Table 8. Combined Impacts on National Economy–Visitor Spending and Payroll

Impact Measure	Visitor Spending Impacts[a]	NPS Payroll Impacts	Combined Impacts	Visitor Spending Share
Direct Effects				
Jobs	139,725	26,031	165,756	84%
Labor Income ($ Millions)	3,961	1,709	5,670	70%
Value Added ($ Millions)	6,313	1,709	8,022	79%
Total Effects				
Jobs	258,416	41,689	300,104	86%
Labor Income ($ Millions)	9,812	2,413	12,225	80%
Value Added ($ Millions)	16,623	2,959	19,582	85%

State-by-State Impact Estimates

Economic impacts of individual parks can be aggregated to the state level with a few complications. While most parks fall within a single state, there are 20 park units with facilities in more than one state. For these parks, shares of visits were assigned to each state based on percentages provided by the NPS Public Use Statistics Office. It was assumed that spending and economic impacts are proportional to where recreation visits are assigned.

Estimates of recreation visits, spending, and local economic impacts for each state and U.S. territory are given in Table A-4 in the Appendix. States receiving the greatest economic effects from NPS visitor and payroll spending are California; Washington, D.C.; Arizona; North Carolina; Utah; and Wyoming. Regional totals are given in Table A-5.

It should be noted that the state and regional totals represent an accumulation of local impacts within roughly 60 miles of each park. The total economic effects on each state or region would be much larger if we included all spending of NPS visitors within each state and used statewide multipliers instead of local ones to capture the secondary effects. As noted earlier, impacts reported here do not include long-distance travel, airfares, or purchases made at home for items that may be used on trips to national parks.

METHODS

Spending and impacts were estimated using the MGM2 model. NPS public use statistics for calendar year 2010 provide estimates of the number of recreation visits and overnight stays at each park. For each park, recreation visits were allocated to the seven MGM2 segments,[13] converted to party days/nights spent in the local area and then multiplied by per-day spending averages for each segment. Spending and impact estimates for 2010 are made individually for each park unit and then summed to obtain national totals for impacts on local regions. Impacts on the national economy are also estimated by applying all visitor spending to multipliers for the national economy.

Spending averages cover all trip expenses within roughly 60 miles of the park. They therefore exclude most en route expenses on longer trips, as well as airfares and purchases made at home in preparation for the trip, including costs of durable goods and equipment. Spending averages vary from park to park based on the type of park and the regional setting (low, medium, or high spending area).

The segment mix is very important in estimating visitor spending, as spending varies considerably across the MGM2 segments. Segment shares are estimated based on park overnight stay data and, where available, park visitor surveys. For park units that lack recent visitor surveys, estimates are made by generalizing from studies at similar parks or based on manager or researcher judgment.

For parks with VSP (Visitor Services Project) studies over the past ten years, spending averages are estimated from the visitor survey data at each park.[14] Averages estimated in the surveys were price adjusted to 2010 using BLS price indices for each spending category. Sampling errors for the spending averages in VSP studies are generally 5–10% overall and can be as high as 20% for individual visitor segments.

The observed spending patterns in park visitor studies are then used to estimate spending averages for other parks that lack visitor spending surveys. This procedure will not capture some spending variations attributable to unique characteristics of a given park or gateway region—for example, the wider use of public transportation at Alaska parks or extra expenses for special commercial attractions in or around some parks, such as rafting trips, air overflights, and other tours. When visitor studies are conducted at individual parks, these unique situations are taken into account.

Multipliers for local regions around national parks were applied to the spending totals to translate spending into jobs, income, and value added and also to estimate secondary effects. All MGM2 multipliers were re-estimated last year using IMPLAN ver 3.0 and 2008 economic data (Minnesota IMPLAN Group 2009). The multipliers have been adjusted to 2010 based on structural changes in the national IMPLAN models between 2008 and 2009 and price changes between 2009 and 2010.

Based on national IMPLAN models, there were some significant structural changes in economic ratios and multipliers between 2008 and 2009. Most notable, was a change in ratios for the amusements sector (IMPLAN sector 410) due to an inflated estimate of output in 2008. IMPLAN ratios in 2009 for sector 410 were more than double the 2008 estimates. This caused a significant underestimate of jobs, income and value added in the MGM2 amusements sector estimates last year. In addition, there were increases of 15-30% in the ratios for retail trade sectors between 2008 and 2009. Ratios for the hotel sector (IMPLAN sector 411) declined by roughly 10%. The MGM2 estimates of jobs, income and value added are sensitive to any changes in these ratios and multipliers.

With the exception of parks with new visitor surveys in 2010, no changes were made in party sizes, lengths of stay, or re-entry factors between 2009 and 2010. MGM2 model parameters for individual parks are adjusted over time as new park visitor studies are conducted or other relevant information becomes available.

Impacts of park payrolls were estimated for each park by applying local area multipliers to NPS wage and salary figures for FY 2010. Multipliers capture the induced effects of park employee spending by re-circulating their income as household spending within the local economy. Payroll benefits (e.g.

contributions to retirement and health insurance) were not re-circulated in estimating secondary effects of park employee spending, but the direct payroll benefits are included in total value added. Multipliers for IMPLAN sector 439 (federal government payroll) were applied to wages and salaries at each park to estimate induced effects.[15] Local impacts of park purchases of supplies and services or construction activities were not included in the analysis.

The number of employees for each park was estimated by totaling the number of distinct social security numbers in each pay period and dividing by the number of pay periods. T

he figure is therefore an annual average. Four seasonal jobs for three months count as one job. No distinction is made between part-time and full-time employees. Jobs, salary, and payroll benefits are assigned to the park where the employee's time was charged, which may differ from their duty station.

Spending and impact totals for states were developed from the 2010 estimates by summing the results for all units in a given state using the mailing address for the park to identify the state. Twenty parks have facilities in more than one state. For these parks, visitors and spending were allocated to individual states based on shares used by the NPS Public Use Statistics Office for allocating visits to states.

For example, visits to Great Smoky Mountains NP were split 44% to North Carolina and 56% to Tennessee. It should be noted that these allocations may not fully account for where the spending and impacts occur. There are also many other parks with facilities in a single state but located within 60 miles of a state border. A portion of the spending and impacts for these parks may accrue to nearby states.

ERRORS AND LIMITATIONS

The accuracy of the spending and impact estimates rests largely on the input data, namely (1) public use recreation visit and overnight stay data; (2) party size, length of stay, and park re-entry conversion factors; (3) visitor segment shares; (4) spending averages; and (5) local area multipliers.

Public use data provides reasonably accurate estimates of visitor entries for most parks. Some visitors may be missed by the counting procedures, while others may be counted multiple times when they re-enter a park more than once on a single trip.

Accurate estimates of park re-entries, party sizes, and lengths of stay in the area are needed to convert park entries to the number of visitor or party days in the region. Visitors staying overnight outside the park pose significant problems as they tend to be the greatest spenders and may enter the park several times during their stay. Similarly, visitors staying inside the park may enter and leave several times during their stay and be counted each time as a distinct visit. Re-entry factors adjust for these problems to the extent possible.

For multi-purpose trips, it is difficult to determine what portion of the spending should be attributed to the park visit. This is especially a problem for historic sites and parks in urban areas or parks in multiple-attraction destinations. For parks with visitor surveys, the proportion of days and spending counted was decided based on stated trip purposes and the importance of the park in generating the trip to the region.

Parkways and urban parks pose special difficulties for economic impact analyses. These units have some of the highest number of visits while posing the most difficult problems for estimating visits, spending, and impacts. The majority of visits to these types of units were assumed to be local or non-local day trips, and only one night of spending was counted for overnight trips. Due to the high numbers of visits at these units, small changes in assumed spending averages or segment mixes can swing the spending estimates by substantial amounts.

Clusters of parks within a single 60-mile area pose additional difficulties. For example, the many monuments and parks in the Washington, D.C., area each count visitors separately. Similar difficulties exist for clusters of parks in Boston, New York, and San Francisco. To avoid double counting of spending across many national capital parks, we must know how many times a visitor has been counted at park units during a trip to the Washington, D.C., area. For parks in the National Capital Region, we currently assume an average of 1.7 park visits are counted for local day trips, 3.4 visits for non-local day trips, and 5.1 park visits on overnight trips. The non-local visitor spending total for the National Capital Region in 2010 was $1.17 billion. This is 14% of the Travel Industry Association tourist spending estimate of $8.3 billion for Washington, D.C., in 2008 (USTA 2010).

NPS units in Alaska also pose special problems for economic analysis. Spending opportunities near Alaska parks are limited and for many visitors the park visit is part of a cruise or guided tour, frequently purchased as a package. Most visitors are on extended trips to Alaska, making it difficult to allocate expenses to a particular park visit. Lodging, vehicle rentals, and air expenses frequently occur in Anchorage, many miles from the park. Also, many Alaska parks are only accessible by air or boat, so spending profiles estimated from visitor surveys at parks in the lower 48 states do not apply well. Due to the prominence of cruise lines and package tours, special studies are required to estimate the proportion of visitor spending that stays in the local regions around national park units in Alaska. In this report, Alaska statewide multipliers are used to estimate impacts for parks in Alaska.

A visit to one or more national parks is an important part of the trip for most Alaska visitors. One could therefore argue to count a substantial portion of tourism spending in Alaska as related to national park visits. The U.S. Travel Association estimated tourist spending in Alaska at $2.1 billion in 2008 (USTA 2010). This is ten times what we have included as spending by park visitors in the local regions around Alaska national parks. Including spending in Alaska outside the local regions would significantly increase the estimates; however, deciding which spending to include would be somewhat subjective.

REFERENCES

Minnesota IMPLAN Group Inc. 2009. IMPLAN Pro Version 3.0, user's guide. Stillwater, Minnesota.

Street, B. 2011. Statistical abstract: 2010. Natural Resource Data Series NPS/NRPC/SSD/NRDS—2011/147. National Park Service, Fort Collins, Colorado.

Stynes, D.J. 2010. Economic benefits to local communities from national park visitation and payroll, 2009. Natural Resources Report NPS/NRPC/SSD/NRR –2010/281. National Park Service, Fort Collins, Colorado.

Stynes, D. J., D. B. Propst, W. H. Chang, and Y. Sun. 2000. Estimating regional economic impacts of park visitor spending: Money Generation Model Version 2 (MGM2). Department of Park, Recreation and Tourism Resources, Michigan State University, East Lansing, Michigan.

U.S. Travel Association (USTA). 2010. The power of travel, economic impact of travel and tourism. Available at http://www.poweroftravel.org /statistics/.

APPENDICES

Table A-1. Spending and Economic Impacts of National Park Visitors on Local Economies, CY 2010

	Public Use Data		Visitor Spending 2010		Impacts of Non-Local Visitor Spending		
Park Unit	2010 Recreation Visits	2010 Overnight Stays	All Visitors ($000's)	Non-Local Visitors ($000's)	Jobs	Labor Income ($000's)	Value Added ($000's)
Abraham Lincoln Birthplace NHP	177,122	0	6,167	5,740	97	2,720	4,436
Acadia NP	2,504,208	159,631	186,282	183,491	3,147	79,636	130,084
Adams NHP	73,339	0	4,742	4,414	66	2,581	4,199
Agate Fossil Beds NM	12,509	0	760	754	13	276	445
Alibates Flint Quarries NM	4,350	0	216	201	3	68	105
Allegheny Portage Railroad NHS	107,363	0	5,340	4,971	82	2,033	3,280
Amistad NRA	1,574,322	27,781	45,348	39,475	615	12,711	20,656
Andersonville NHS	121,535	0	4,232	3,939	68	1,600	2,609
Andrew Johnson NHS	60,323	0	3,001	2,793	45	1,249	2,044
Antietam NB	393,957	0	19,347	17,429	250	9,493	15,663
*Apostle Islands NL	156,945	24,358	17,281	16,920	287	6,359	10,008
Appomattox Court House NHP	216,220	0	10,755	10,010	158	3,925	6,469
*Arches NP	1,014,405	47,112	105,132	105,132	1,659	37,449	60,742
Arkansas Post NMEM	34,712	0	1,209	1,125	20	369	607
Arlington House, Robert E. Lee MEM	627,576	0	40,581	37,771	450	18,670	30,129
Assateague Island NS	2,106,090	82,461	142,650	135,543	2,041	59,120	97,895
Aztec Ruins NM	37,437	0	1,172	1,135	16	435	716
*Badlands NP	977,778	36,506	23,177	23,177	375	9,189	14,990
Bandelier NM	234,896	7,263	10,507	10,152	121	2,789	4,434
Bent's Old Fort NHS	29,120	0	1,014	944	14	306	497
Bering Land Bridge NPRES	2,642	1,123	833	833	9	322	554
Big Bend NP	372,330	175,574	16,121	15,423	231	5,336	8,969
Big Cypress NPRES	665,523	16,418	78,758	77,146	1,149	41,721	67,505
Big Hole NB	44,771	0	1,559	1,451	25	541	895
Big South Fork NRRA	656,374	65,160	26,575	23,218	331	7,797	12,567
Big Thicket NPRES	140,489	1,932	9,521	9,040	132	4,466	7,682
Bighorn Canyon NRA	258,637	20,577	7,567	6,630	106	2,723	4,518
Biscayne NP	467,612	12,702	30,721	30,358	407	14,543	23,786
Black Canyon of the Gunnison NP	176,344	16,400	8,334	7,929	112	2,781	4,610
Blue Ridge Parkway	14,517,118	150,520	299,787	274,134	4,008	87,995	142,233

	Public Use Data		Visitor Spending 2010		Impacts of Non-Local Visitor Spending		
Park Unit	2010 Recreation Visits	2010 Overnight Stays	All Visitors ($000's)	Non-Local Visitors ($000's)	Jobs	Labor Income ($000's)	Value Added ($000's)
Bluestone NSR	37,790	0	1,610	1,407	18	359	562
Booker T. Washington NM	21,665	0	1,078	1,003	17	422	691
Boston African American NHS	333,463	0	21,563	20,070	259	10,889	17,560
Boston NHP	2,060,497	0	72,023	69,624	904	38,412	62,525
Brown V. Board of Education NHS	17,808	0	886	824	14	409	698
Bryce Canyon NP	1,285,492	146,965	107,904	106,864	1,667	34,869	57,707
Buck Island Reef NM	27,403	3,920	1,846	1,758	27	591	965
Buffalo National River	1,545,599	114,898	47,169	41,554	594	14,794	24,310
Cabrillo NM	763,140	0	49,347	45,930	613	21,142	34,738
Canaveral NS	966,099	2,702	65,558	62,234	990	32,397	53,679
Cane River Creole NHP	25,115	0	1,249	1,163	19	435	701
Canyon de Chelly NM	827,247	50,502	40,641	37,879	537	12,832	21,022
Canyonlands NP	435,908	88,191	34,633	34,291	474	12,713	21,154
Cape Cod NS	4,653,706	22,725	171,182	136,191	1,856	66,005	108,739
Cape Hatteras NS	2,193,292	84,393	108,475	103,084	1,615	42,057	69,452
Cape Krusenstern NM	2,521	427	794	794	9	304	520
Cape Lookout NS	530,181	29,268	37,276	35,501	572	12,749	20,852
Capitol Reef NP	662,661	38,566	37,958	37,740	649	13,025	21,439
*Capulin Volcano NM	48,580	0	1,341	1,316	18	360	590
Carl Sandburg Home NHS	86,740	0	4,315	4,016	61	1,593	2,581
Carlsbad Caverns NP	428,524	170	23,328	22,744	346	7,225	11,843
Casa Grande Ruins NM	77,347	0	2,259	2,121	23	585	903
Castillo de San Marcos NM	708,549	0	45,817	42,644	581	17,342	28,697
Castle Clinton NM	4,126,378	0	77,409	53,845	619	27,171	44,063
Catoctin Mountain Park	385,745	33,134	19,576	18,299	217	9,022	14,477
Cedar Breaks NM	525,831	0	18,309	17,041	274	6,674	10,962
Chaco Culture NHP	34,226	9,829	925	891	12	282	459
Chamizal NMEM	226,535	0	14,649	13,634	232	5,659	9,536
Channel Islands NP	277,515	59,584	24,004	22,881	300	11,357	18,568
Charles Pinckney NHS	44,081	0	2,193	2,041	32	901	1,505
Chattahoochee River NRA	3,011,393	0	89,784	60,449	780	28,133	46,090
*Chesapeake & Ohio Canal NHP	4,111,238	10,231	53,103	33,842	453	18,184	29,230
Chickamauga & Chattanooga NMP	991,901	2,204	49,364	45,951	724	21,928	36,116
Chickasaw NRA	1,253,637	66,127	17,157	13,276	174	3,798	6,200
Chiricahua NM	55,436	8,521	2,859	2,681	35	900	1,453
Christiansted NHS	117,214	0	4,081	3,799	58	1,269	2,071
City of Rocks NRES	92,484	0	6,278	5,959	85	2,078	3,361
Clara Barton NHS	23,741	0	1,535	1,429	17	706	1,140
*Colonial NHP	3,459,965	0	60,693	55,798	913	23,734	39,897

Table A-1. (Continued)

Park Unit	Public Use Data		Visitor Spending 2010		Impacts of Non-Local Visitor Spending		
	2010 Recreation Visits	2010 Overnight Stays	All Visitors ($000's)	Non-Local Visitors ($000's)	Jobs	Labor Income ($000's)	Value Added ($000's)
Colorado NM	433,561	17,300	21,766	20,299	292	7,596	12,389
Congaree NP	121,208	4,981	2,788	2,466	44	1,132	1,877
Coronado NMEM	136,284	0	4,745	4,417	63	1,779	2,910
Cowpens NB	226,868	17	11,284	10,503	180	4,770	7,901
*Crater Lake NP	448,319	80,467	34,111	33,088	540	13,393	21,887
*Craters of the Moon NM & PRES	215,698	14,856	6,732	6,660	95	2,117	3,440
Cumberland Gap NHP	918,746	15,917	45,833	42,693	695	14,723	23,831
Cumberland Island NS	91,996	17,979	6,156	5,869	92	2,922	4,826
Curecanti NRA	969,549	54,667	40,364	35,295	478	11,899	19,545
Cuyahoga Valley NP	2,492,670	2,719	54,677	39,446	599	17,681	28,912
*Dayton Aviation Heritage NHP	63,961	0	3,268	3,092	57	1,472	2,407
De Soto NMEM	265,406	0	17,162	15,974	268	8,622	14,247
Death Valley NP	984,775	221,614	48,620	46,529	517	13,733	21,544
Delaware Water Gap NRA	5,285,761	104,558	151,261	129,257	2,087	57,652	93,307
*Denali NP & PRES	378,855	106,108	141,415	141,415	1,822	56,211	83,330
Devils Postpile NM	80,349	4,444	2,835	2,646	38	1,081	1,749
Devils Tower NM	436,200	15,939	15,321	14,286	229	5,643	9,295
Dinosaur NM	197,812	49,659	6,717	6,291	77	2,203	3,655
Dry Tortugas NP	53,890	13,786	4,689	4,480	52	1,899	3,147
Edgar Allan Poe NHS	16,584	0	1,072	998	15	554	910
*Effigy Mounds NM	79,783	0	4,625	4,431	80	1,513	2,442
*Eisenhower NHS	61,210	0	3,845	3,814	64	1,461	2,368
El Malpais NM	134,662	680	4,924	4,742	79	2,133	3,513
El Morro NM	52,566	2,525	1,834	1,756	25	536	889
Eleanor Roosevelt NHS	53,067	0	907	561	8	232	377
Eugene O'Neill NHS	2,445	0	158	147	2	82	137
*Everglades NP	915,538	33,110	136,494	131,383	1,956	72,196	117,401
Federal Hall NMEM	178,749	0	11,559	10,758	124	6,016	9,808
Fire Island NS	613,057	43,656	35,076	30,753	390	15,827	25,886
First Ladies NHS	8,766	0	567	528	9	205	332
Flight 93 NMEM	137,837	0	6,856	6,381	102	2,465	3,976
Florissant Fossil Beds NM	65,422	0	3,254	3,029	41	1,230	2,025
Ford's Theatre NHS	662,298	0	21,476	19,661	234	9,930	16,277
Fort Bowie NHS	9,491	0	472	439	6	150	243
Fort Caroline NMEM	299,906	0	19,393	18,050	283	8,997	14,846
Fort Davis NHS	43,280	0	1,507	1,403	21	454	752
Fort Donelson NB	202,210	32	7,041	6,553	105	2,241	3,661
Fort Frederica NM	294,484	0	14,648	13,634	201	5,524	9,044

Park Unit	Public Use Data		Visitor Spending 2010		Impacts of Non-Local Visitor Spending		
	2010 Recreation Visits	2010 Overnight Stays	All Visitors ($000's)	Non-Local Visitors ($000's)	Jobs	Labor Income ($000's)	Value Added ($000's)
Fort Laramie NHS	57,128	0	1,989	1,851	29	673	1,119
*Fort Larned NHS	29,423	0	1,598	1,563	28	560	916
Fort Matanzas NM	673,700	0	43,564	40,547	552	16,489	27,286
Fort McHenry NM & HS	611,582	0	39,547	36,808	483	15,641	25,463
Fort Necessity NB	264,450	1,105	8,453	7,427	113	2,594	4,174
Fort Point NHS	1,315,241	0	85,048	79,158	879	40,929	67,094
Fort Pulaski NM	416,292	29	20,707	19,273	295	8,601	14,244
Fort Raleigh NHS	305,711	0	10,644	9,907	161	4,192	7,002
Fort Scott NHS	27,635	0	962	896	15	298	481
Fort Smith NHS	68,678	0	3,416	3,180	57	1,261	2,047
*Fort Stanwix NM	103,748	0	3,795	3,632	54	1,425	2,260
Fort Sumter NM	797,713	2	18,408	16,389	238	6,422	10,521
Fort Union NM	10,638	0	631	631	9	210	351
Fort Union Trading Post NHS	14,458	0	985	955	15	322	528
Fort Vancouver NHS	786,989	0	39,146	36,435	625	19,724	32,614
Fort Washington Park	352,883	0	11,443	10,476	125	5,291	8,672
Fossil Butte NM	19,700	0	840	840	12	280	470
Franklin Delano Roosevelt Memorial	2,238,052	0	72,571	66,441	792	33,554	55,002
Frederick Douglass NHS	44,699	0	1,449	1,327	16	670	1,099
Frederick Law Olmsted NHS	3,285	0	212	198	3	107	173
Fredericksburg & Spotsylvania NMP	899,936	0	44,764	41,664	595	15,755	26,228
Friendship Hill NHS	32,562	0	2,106	1,960	31	723	1,183
Gates of the Arctic NP & PRES	10,840	7,175	3,422	3,422	39	1,329	2,303
Gateway NRA	8,820,757	12,985	161,040	65,265	750	35,747	58,536
Gauley River NRA	107,223	4,082	4,440	3,875	58	1,511	2,451
General Grant NMEM	119,665	0	7,738	7,202	83	4,028	6,566
George Rogers Clark NHP	118,912	0	5,915	5,505	92	1,822	2,959
*George Washington Birthplace NM	128,158	0	2,964	1,868	28	591	971
George Washington Carver NM	35,068	0	546	546	8	190	305
George Washington MEM PKWY	6,925,099	0	29,729	4,337	51	1,990	3,215
*Gettysburg NMP	1,031,554	25,944	63,573	63,066	1,051	24,153	39,159
Gila Cliff Dwellings NM	32,652	0	861	830	13	238	388
Glacier Bay NP & PRES	444,530	15,221	3,161	3,161	40	1,329	2,259
Glacier NP	2,200,048	372,371	108,880	104,690	1,632	41,958	70,696
Glen Canyon NRA	2,124,467	1,600,687	181,609	181,609	2,278	68,395	100,298

Table A-1. (Continued)

Park Unit	Public Use Data		Visitor Spending 2010		Impacts of Non-Local Visitor Spending		
	2010 Recreation Visits	2010 Overnight Stays	All Visitors ($000's)	Non-Local Visitors ($000's)	Jobs	Labor Income ($000's)	Value Added ($000's)
Golden Gate NRA	14,271,503	57,499	264,151	109,666	1,451	59,795	99,870
*Golden Spike NHS	43,561	0	2,068	2,019	32	756	1,224
Governors Island NM	409,207	0	36,111	34,278	397	19,442	31,718
*Grand Canyon NP	4,388,386	1,245,883	415,797	415,797	6,167	167,945	265,834
Grand Portage NM	113,996	210	12,569	12,506	197	4,510	7,495
*Grand Teton NP	2,669,374	517,670	424,041	420,201	6,258	162,404	269,247
Grant-Kohrs Ranch NHS	22,075	0	769	715	12	305	509
Great Basin NP	88,870	35,933	4,128	3,959	55	1,149	1,856
Great Sand Dunes NP & PRES	283,284	49,826	10,231	9,602	141	3,291	5,365
Great Smoky Mountains NP	9,463,538	393,812	818,195	792,547	11,367	303,510	504,948
Greenbelt Park	270,661	55,747	18,366	17,266	203	8,483	13,511
Guadalupe Mountains NP	192,210	17,445	12,973	12,341	193	3,730	6,158
Guilford Courthouse NMP	285,444	7	14,198	13,215	228	6,276	10,182
Gulf Islands NS	4,283,747	69,973	118,718	68,675	1,006	26,759	44,172
Hagerman Fossil Beds NM	29,795	0	901	787	13	294	480
Haleakala NP	1,105,606	21,126	74,966	71,195	861	32,974	54,523
Hamilton Grange NMEM	0	0	0	0	0	0	0
Hampton NHS	32,153	0	2,079	1,935	25	822	1,339
Harpers Ferry NHP	268,822	0	10,000	9,134	129	4,051	6,556
Harry S Truman NHS	27,670	0	1,789	1,665	28	926	1,577
Hawaii Volcanoes NP	1,304,667	77,320	88,258	83,901	1,162	40,232	66,892
Herbert Hoover NHS	142,512	0	7,089	6,598	111	2,735	4,524
Home of Franklin D. Roosevelt NHS	140,251	0	2,852	2,509	36	1,058	1,719
*Homestead National Monument of America	74,314	0	2,265	2,121	36	789	1,272
Hopewell Culture NHP	33,918	0	1,181	1,099	17	381	615
Hopewell Furnace NHS	55,750	0	2,773	2,581	41	1,210	1,972
Horseshoe Bend NMP	67,776	0	3,371	3,138	51	1,100	1,796
Hot Springs NP	1,311,807	12,409	89,001	84,505	1,411	30,685	50,436
Hovenweep NM	27,386	1,696	1,382	1,291	18	485	807
Hubbell Trading Post NHS	80,578	0	4,008	3,730	53	1,121	1,901
Independence NHP	3,751,007	0	146,515	131,163	1,915	69,968	115,401
Indiana Dunes NL	2,150,345	24,401	63,495	44,456	658	16,276	26,706
Isle Royale NP	15,793	48,953	1,959	1,959	29	640	1,056
*James A. Garfield NHS	24,853	0	766	700	11	341	566
Jean Lafitte NHP & PRES	391,019	0	19,450	18,103	260	9,081	15,107

	Public Use Data		Visitor Spending 2010		Impacts of Non-Local Visitor Spending		
Park Unit	2010 Recreation Visits	2010 Overnight Stays	All Visitors ($000's)	Non-Local Visitors ($000's)	Jobs	Labor Income ($000's)	Value Added ($000's)
Jefferson National Expansion Memorial	2,436,110	0	98,436	86,619	1,309	37,404	60,984
Jewel Cave NM	103,462	0	5,146	4,790	82	1,955	3,224
Jimmy Carter NHS	64,849	0	2,258	2,102	36	687	1,114
John D Rockefeller Jr. MEM PKWY	1,222,931	33,531	7,063	6,527	90	2,336	3,818
*John Day Fossil Beds NM	135,151	5	6,119	6,025	75	1,674	2,752
John F. Kennedy NHS	17,466	0	1,129	1,051	14	570	920
John Muir NHS	34,904	0	2,257	2,101	30	1,004	1,663
Johnstown Flood NMEM	100,799	0	5,704	5,274	93	2,293	3,728
*Joshua Tree NP	1,434,976	287,765	37,485	32,677	378	11,892	18,926
Kalaupapa NHP	27,919	0	1,389	1,293	16	591	973
Kaloko-Honokohau NHP	132,731	0	6,602	6,145	85	2,921	4,841
*Katmai NP & PRES/Aniakchak NM & PRES	55,172	6,697	13,102	12,952	133	3,686	5,778
Kenai Fjords NP	297,596	2,976	9,468	9,331	129	4,156	7,080
Kennesaw Mountain NBP	1,512,191	0	47,531	41,342	582	20,220	33,291
*Kings Mountain NMP	275,555	86	9,469	8,449	136	3,114	5,149
Klondike Gold Rush NHP Alaska	797,716	7,237	20,821	20,572	267	8,769	14,882
Klondike Gold Rush NHP Seattle	65,870	0	4,259	3,964	59	2,143	3,568
Knife River Indian Villages NHS	21,721	0	756	704	13	297	485
Kobuk Valley NP	3,164	503	996	996	11	382	653
Korean War Veterans Memorial	3,072,716	0	99,636	91,219	1,087	46,068	75,515
Lake Chelan NRA	39,249	10,200	1,555	1,426	20	760	1,272
Lake Clark NP & PRES	9,931	5,149	3,133	3,133	35	1,212	2,093
Lake Mead NRA	7,080,758	770,988	254,878	216,693	2,452	84,942	132,977
Lake Meredith NRA	883,586	22,249	36,452	31,762	435	10,337	16,026
Lake Roosevelt NRA	1,324,074	159,938	39,811	35,121	515	12,807	20,755
Lassen Volcanic NP	384,570	98,686	16,053	14,634	207	5,933	9,403
Lava Beds NM	130,765	9,915	4,494	4,288	56	1,408	2,263
LBJ Memorial Grove on the Potomac	230,694	0	14,917	13,884	165	6,863	11,075
Lewis & Clark NHP	218,553	0	10,871	10,118	154	3,380	5,515
Lincoln Boyhood NMEM	126,228	0	6,279	5,844	97	2,049	3,356
Lincoln Home NHS	354,125	0	18,516	18,178	285	7,796	12,568
Lincoln Memorial	6,042,315	0	195,929	179,377	2,138	90,590	148,495
Little Bighorn Battlefield NM	320,959	0	11,175	10,402	174	4,438	7,401

Table A-1. (Continued)

Park Unit	Public Use Data		Visitor Spending 2010		Impacts of Non-Local Visitor Spending		
	2010 Recreation Visits	2010 Overnight Stays	All Visitors ($000's)	Non-Local Visitors ($000's)	Jobs	Labor Income ($000's)	Value Added ($000's)
Little River Canyon NPRES	192,576	0	9,151	8,686	149	3,141	5,138
Little Rock Central High School NHS	49,740	0	2,474	2,303	38	1,118	1,817
Longfellow NHS	45,684	0	2,272	2,115	28	1,037	1,684
Lowell NHP	540,475	0	34,949	32,529	435	15,947	25,897
Lyndon B. Johnson NHP	112,680	0	7,286	6,782	93	2,911	4,811
Maggie L Walker NHS	12,331	0	291	154	2	74	123
Mammoth Cave NP	497,225	84,484	32,841	31,052	530	12,290	19,826
Manassas NBP	612,490	0	8,267	7,911	97	3,333	5,462
*Manzanar NHS	76,592	0	7,565	7,518	87	2,351	3,887
Marsh-Billings-Rockefeller NHP	31,209	0	1,552	1,445	21	617	1,016
Martin Luther King, Jr. NHS	658,452	0	42,578	39,629	532	19,950	32,839
Martin Van Buren NHS	21,055	0	418	365	5	139	219
Mary McLeod Bethune Council House NHS	19,520	0	633	579	7	293	480
Mesa Verde NP	559,712	95,496	41,346	39,597	560	14,816	24,238
Minute Man NHP	1,073,748	0	69,432	64,624	865	31,682	51,449
*Minuteman Missile NHS	42,348	0	2,811	2,811	46	1,137	1,881
Missouri National Recreational River	167,301	0	7,950	7,546	156	2,325	3,800
Mojave NPRES	600,897	1,744	12,891	11,255	142	5,078	8,236
*Monocacy NB	33,313	0	2,399	2,227	27	1,071	1,782
Montezuma Castle NM	578,554	0	28,778	26,785	415	13,872	23,113
Moores Creek NB	51,326	271	1,783	1,660	29	678	1,140
Morristown NHP	278,392	0	13,848	12,889	168	6,401	10,482
*Mount Rainier NP	1,191,754	172,838	35,389	33,696	484	14,150	22,832
Mount Rushmore NMEM	2,331,237	0	77,157	72,619	1,174	27,975	45,607
Muir Woods NM	834,356	0	53,952	50,216	643	27,440	45,733
Natchez NHP	206,870	0	10,290	9,577	136	3,015	5,027
Natchez Trace PKWY	5,910,950	21,201	88,326	32,079	454	9,959	15,958
National Capital Parks-Central	1,363,389	0	44,210	40,475	482	20,441	33,507
National Capital Parks-East	1,181,960	0	38,326	35,089	418	17,721	29,048
Natural Bridges NM	95,676	5,781	4,828	4,507	64	1,410	2,346
Navajo NM	90,696	2,933	4,538	4,230	56	1,504	2,443
New Bedford Whaling NHP	277,681	0	12,215	12,215	202	6,461	10,587
New Orleans Jazz NHP	80,195	0	3,989	3,713	53	1,862	3,098

	Public Use Data		Visitor Spending 2010		Impacts of Non-Local Visitor Spending		
Park Unit	2010 Recreation Visits	2010 Overnight Stays	All Visitors ($000's)	Non-Local Visitors ($000's)	Jobs	Labor Income ($000's)	Value Added ($000's)
*New River Gorge NR	1,151,213	10,008	46,023	43,266	553	10,761	16,934
Nez Perce NHP	193,000	0	6,720	6,255	106	2,362	3,840
Nicodemus NHS	3,448	0	156	152	2	37	57
Ninety Six NHS	63,747	0	3,171	2,951	48	1,013	1,654
Niobrara NSR	69,705	0	3,312	3,144	65	969	1,583
Noatak NPRES	3,257	540	1,026	1,026	12	393	672
North Cascades NP	24,659	17,801	1,535	1,474	21	770	1,289
Obed Wild and Scenic River	180,203	1,269	7,692	6,727	105	2,466	3,945
Ocmulgee NM	109,413	0	5,442	5,065	88	2,166	3,558
*Olympic NP	2,844,563	300,891	103,099	94,596	1,395	34,906	57,102
Oregon Caves NM	86,335	6,560	4,113	3,829	62	1,559	2,529
Organ Pipe Cactus NM	209,602	23,690	10,692	10,007	156	5,182	8,624
Ozark National Scenic Riverways	1,416,529	173,952	63,351	56,183	888	19,332	30,592
Padre Island NS	612,716	67,261	41,287	39,292	640	16,806	27,603
Palo Alto Battlefield NHP	26,865	0	935	871	15	356	581
Pea Ridge NMP	115,128	0	5,727	5,330	96	1,747	2,875
Pecos NHP	33,864	0	736	712	11	319	524
Pennsylvania Avenue NHS	262,030	0	8,497	7,779	93	3,929	6,440
*Perry's Victory and International Peace MEM	92,944	1,685	7,150	7,150	145	3,494	5,686
Petersburg NB	175,553	0	8,732	8,127	137	3,447	5,783
Petrified Forest NP	664,725	300	45,120	42,830	641	14,963	24,659
Petroglyph NM	105,643	0	4,399	3,576	62	1,715	2,846
*Pictured Rocks NL	499,281	28,855	20,955	20,596	339	5,297	8,615
Pinnacles NM	246,575	10,360	4,836	4,034	48	1,782	2,928
Pipe Spring NM	59,952	0	2,982	2,776	39	1,049	1,706
Pipestone NM	78,108	0	3,362	3,264	56	1,438	2,363
Piscataway Park	248,314	0	8,052	7,372	88	3,723	6,103
Point Reyes NS	2,067,271	39,421	84,725	77,224	981	41,182	67,880
President's Park	616,635	0	19,995	18,306	218	9,245	15,154
Prince William Forest Park	386,521	49,050	20,715	15,517	185	7,775	12,005
Pu'uhonua o Honaunau NHP	419,590	0	20,871	19,426	269	9,233	15,303
Puukohola Heiau NHS	129,886	0	6,461	6,013	83	2,858	4,737
Rainbow Bridge NM	104,501	0	5,198	4,838	62	1,687	2,719
Redwood NP	418,820	7,479	20,717	18,693	268	6,565	10,453
Richmond NBP	130,415	0	9,194	8,293	134	4,042	6,700
Rio Grande Wild and Scenic River	1,103	6,046	121	119	2	36	60
Rock Creek Park	1,883,457	0	61,073	55,914	666	28,238	46,288
Rocky Mountain NP	2,955,821	174,202	170,804	170,804	2,641	77,625	129,666

Table A-1. (Continued)

Park Unit	Public Use Data		Visitor Spending 2010		Impacts of Non-Local Visitor Spending		
	2010 Recreation Visits	2010 Overnight Stays	All Visitors ($000's)	Non-Local Visitors ($000's)	Jobs	Labor Income ($000's)	Value Added ($000's)
Roger Williams NMEM	51,559	0	3,334	3,103	49	1,653	2,674
Ross Lake NRA	682,736	67,898	20,458	18,008	254	9,369	15,616
Russell Cave NM	23,374	0	1,163	1,082	18	363	589
Sagamore Hill NHS	55,149	0	3,566	3,319	42	1,726	2,820
Saguaro NP	717,614	1,568	24,161	16,752	229	6,426	10,477
Saint Croix NSR	188,400	25,884	5,660	4,990	80	2,166	3,534
Saint Paul's Church NHS	16,362	0	1,058	985	11	551	898
*Saint-Gaudens NHS	30,941	0	1,169	1,076	17	477	790
Salem Maritime NHS	806,506	0	52,151	48,540	642	21,185	34,276
Salinas Pueblo Missions NM	32,941	0	847	816	13	373	614
San Antonio Missions NHP	1,304,690	0	50,961	45,622	701	21,159	34,908
San Francisco Maritime NHP	4,130,970	10,946	86,294	63,899	675	30,842	50,167
San Juan Island NHP	263,370	0	17,030	15,851	209	5,949	9,819
San Juan NHS	1,105,252	0	54,976	51,169	781	18,624	30,436
Santa Monica Mountains NRA	568,371	144	22,915	15,196	202	7,572	12,436
Saratoga NHP	63,719	0	2,219	2,065	28	776	1,249
Saugus Iron Works NHS	10,775	0	697	648	8	349	563
Scotts Bluff NM	133,795	0	4,318	3,519	65	1,326	2,102
*Sequoia NP/ Kings Canyon NP[a]	1,320,156	438,677	97,012	89,408	1,283	37,299	60,504
Shenandoah NP	1,253,386	301,700	71,751	63,347	968	25,199	41,107
Shiloh NMP	317,046	0	11,039	10,275	169	3,774	6,295
Sitka NHP	189,176	0	3,784	3,739	49	1,594	2,704
*Sleeping Bear Dunes NL	1,280,932	116,382	120,482	117,346	2,070	54,605	92,417
Springfield Armory NHS	16,876	0	1,091	1,016	15	521	847
Statue of Liberty NM	3,833,288	0	166,402	149,929	1,724	81,161	132,772
Steamtown NHS	104,855	0	3,651	3,398	57	1,582	2,541
Stones River NB	187,559	0	9,329	8,683	133	4,616	7,583
Sunset Crater Volcano NM	158,819	0	7,900	7,353	97	2,691	4,338
Tallgrass Prairie NPRES	22,047	0	1,048	994	16	308	498
Thaddeus Kosciuszko NMEM	2,888	0	187	174	3	97	159
Theodore Roosevelt Birthplace NHS	15,029	0	972	905	10	506	825
Theodore Roosevelt Inaugural NHS	17,491	0	1,131	1,053	17	497	796
Theodore Roosevelt Island Park	116,035	0	7,503	6,984	83	3,452	5,571

Park Unit	Public Use Data		Visitor Spending 2010		Impacts of Non-Local Visitor Spending		
	2010 Recreation Visits	2010 Overnight Stays	All Visitors ($000's)	Non-Local Visitors ($000's)	Jobs	Labor Income ($000's)	Value Added ($000's)
Theodore Roosevelt NP	623,748	28,868	29,562	28,094	503	10,127	16,337
Thomas Edison NHP	63,009	0	4,074	3,792	49	1,951	3,193
Thomas Jefferson Memorial	2,305,856	0	74,770	68,453	816	34,571	56,668
Thomas Stone NHS	6,004	0	388	361	5	137	226
Timpanogos Cave NM	120,241	0	7,775	7,237	124	3,647	5,996
Timucuan Ecological & Historic PRES	993,948	0	50,804	39,677	616	19,560	32,181
Tonto NM	60,497	0	3,009	2,801	44	1,476	2,465
Tumacacori NHP	39,866	0	1,388	1,292	18	520	851
Tuskegee Airmen NHS	60,827	0	3,026	2,816	45	938	1,527
Tuskegee Institute NHS	23,230	0	1,155	1,075	17	358	583
Tuzigoot NM	103,274	0	5,137	4,781	74	2,476	4,126
Ulysses S. Grant NHS	39,967	0	2,584	2,405	37	1,070	1,739
Upper Delaware SRR	306,468	0	9,139	7,987	111	2,927	4,738
*Valley Forge NHP	1,617,511	750	58,195	41,560	631	24,681	40,781
Vanderbilt Mansion NHS	390,525	0	5,674	3,313	45	1,332	2,151
Vicksburg NMP	581,459	0	28,922	26,920	420	11,264	18,301
Vietnam Veterans Memorial	4,555,371	0	147,713	135,234	1,612	68,297	111,952
*Virgin Islands NP	493,477	87,981	61,123	61,123	1,084	25,077	40,089
Voyageurs NP	253,891	90,701	11,934	11,426	193	4,355	7,047
Walnut Canyon NM	126,552	0	6,295	5,859	77	2,144	3,457
War in the Pacific NHP	219,349	0	7,637	7,109	85	3,514	5,670
Washington Monument	628,665	0	20,385	18,663	222	9,425	15,450
Washita Battlefield NHS	12,552	0	489	460	8	153	252
Weir Farm NHS	19,313	0	1,249	1,162	13	590	965
Whiskeytown-Shasta-Trinity NRA	788,065	44,789	32,774	28,653	420	11,504	18,340
White House	922,335	0	29,908	27,381	326	13,828	22,667
White Sands NM	470,921	1,811	16,427	16,109	250	5,157	8,552
Whitman Mission NHS	58,521	0	2,038	1,897	29	721	1,176
William Howard Taft NHS	21,163	0	1,368	1,274	20	629	1,023
Wilson's Creek NB	185,200	0	9,212	8,574	157	3,922	6,343
Wind Cave NP	577,141	3,263	51,500	51,500	925	22,350	37,231
Wolf Trap NP for the Performing Arts	520,397	0	33,651	31,320	373	15,482	24,983
*Women's Rights NHP	22,662	0	623	623	7	182	282
World War II Memorial	3,964,351	0	128,549	117,689	1,403	59,436	97,427
World War II Valor in the Pacific NM	1,372,724	0	53,619	48,001	719	25,114	41,525
Wrangell-St Elias NP & PRES	73,170	0	3,242	3,242	41	1,389	2,407

Table A-1. (Continued)

Park Unit	Public Use Data		Visitor Spending 2010		Impacts of Non-Local Visitor Spending		
	2010 Recreation Visits	2010 Overnight Stays	All Visitors ($000's)	Non-Local Visitors ($000's)	Jobs	Labor Income ($000's)	Value Added ($000's)
Wright Brothers NMEM	476,200	0	16,581	15,432	251	6,531	10,907
Wupatki NM	221,083	0	10,997	10,235	135	3,746	6,039
*Yellowstone NP	3,640,185	1,306,318	334,445	334,445	4,881	135,847	225,635
*Yosemite NP	3,901,408	1,720,909	354,689	350,244	4,602	132,465	215,932
Yukon-Charley Rivers NPRES	6,211	7,102	3,569	3,569	40	1,385	2,398
*Zion NP	2,665,972	304,208	123,727	122,606	2,136	53,476	85,771

a Sequoia and Kings Canyon national parks are combined for the economic analysis. Recreation visits for the two parks are reduced to reflect double counting between the two parks.

* For these parks, results are based on a visitor survey at the designated park. For other parks, visitor characteristics and spending averages are adapted from national averages for each park type, adjusted for surrounding populations and spending opportunities.

Notes: Non-local visitors live outside a roughly 60-mile radius of the park. Jobs include part-time and full-time jobs with seasonal jobs adjusted to an annual basis. Impacts include direct and secondary effects of visitor spending on the local economy. Labor income covers wages and salaries, payroll benefits, and incomes of sole proprietors in the local region. Value added includes labor income, profits and rents, and indirect business taxes.

Table A-2. Payroll Impacts of National Park Units on Local Economies, FY 2010

Park Unit	**Park Payroll**			**Impacts of Park Payroll**		
	Salary ($000's)	**Payroll Benefits ($000's)**	**NPS Jobs**	**Total Jobs**	**Labor Income ($000's)**	**Value Added ($000's)**
Abraham Lincoln Birthplace NHS	764	148	16	21	1,088	1,232
Acadia NP	6,743	1,687	142	184	9,800	10,878
Adams NHS	1,476	309	25	35	2,281	2,652
Agate Fossil Beds NM	464	119	11	14	658	718
Allegheny Portage Railroad NHS	1,464	429	29	38	2,179	2,424
Amistad NRA	1,985	621	40	48	2,806	3,018
Andersonville NHS	923	267	20	24	1,344	1,480
Andrew Johnson NHS	566	132	13	16	827	936
Antietam NB	2,990	811	56	73	4,580	5,220
Apostle Islands NL	2,430	684	36	48	3,438	3,728

Park Unit	Park Payroll			Impacts of Park Payroll		
	Salary ($000's)	Payroll Benefits ($000's)	NPS Jobs	Total Jobs	Labor Income ($000's)	Value Added ($000's)
Appomattox Court House NHP	1,171	314	27	32	1,666	1,847
Arches NP	1,067	308	24	28	1,475	1,586
Arkansas Post NMEM	545	136	14	16	751	823
Arlington House, Robert E. Lee Mem	801	221	21	23	1,165	1,284
Assateague Island NS	3,807	940	85	109	5,574	6,315
Aztec Ruins NM	1,204	318	25	31	1,726	1,917
Badlands NP	3,556	963	81	100	5,166	5,689
Bandelier NM	3,501	1,040	84	85	4,557	4,585
Bent's Old Fort NHS	813	195	20	22	1,083	1,154
Bering Land Bridge NPRES	135	32	3	3	195	221
Big Bend NP	5,756	1,709	123	141	7,959	8,576
Big Cypress NPRES	4,786	1,447	75	104	7,399	8,363
Big South Fork NRRA	3,138	921	56	68	4,408	4,787
Big Thicket NPRES	2,131	648	42	52	3,212	3,608
Bighorn Canyon NRA	2,457	666	47	62	3,618	4,051
Biscayne NP	3,004	888	58	79	4,741	5,455
Black Canyon of the Gunnison NP	1,216	292	29	33	1,620	1,748
Blue Ridge Parkway	11,892	3,336	265	302	16,267	17,385
Bluestone NSR	56	20	1	1	76	76
Booker T. Washington NM	602	189	12	15	903	1,005
Boston African American NHS	459	89	15	17	668	756
Boston NHP	5,803	1,677	88	115	8,992	10,111
Brown V. Board of Education NHS	687	221	13	18	1,084	1,232
Bryce Canyon NP	3,327	886	87	97	4,471	4,773
Buck Island Reef NM	216	52	5	5	287	307
Buffalo National River	4,617	1,412	110	130	6,596	7,196
Cabrillo NM	1,353	367	29	36	1,990	2,229
Canaveral NS	2,511	683	54	73	3,892	4,487
Cane River Creole NHP	760	194	15	18	1,062	1,159
Canyon de Chelly NM	1,816	488	41	46	2,456	2,633
Canyonlands NP	5,549	1,526	134	153	7,649	8,312
Cape Cod NS	6,532	1,640	108	144	9,652	10,981
Cape Hatteras NS	6,372	1,747	140	178	9,368	10,617
Cape Lookout NS	1,985	399	40	48	2,591	2,807
Capitol Reef NP	1,727	499	35	44	2,419	2,628
Capulin Volcano NM	423	111	12	13	559	586
Carl Sandburg Home NHS	930	203	24	28	1,279	1,407
Carlsbad Caverns NP	4,377	1,229	100	114	6,033	6,474
Casa Grande Ruins NM	685	187	15	15	875	877
Castillo de San Marcos NM	2,204	630	46	55	3,134	3,459
Castle Clinton NM	296	74	8	9	440	496
Catoctin Mountain Park	2,390	637	47	55	3,454	3,811

Table A-2. (Continued)

	Park Payroll			Impacts of Park Payroll		
Park Unit	Salary ($000's)	Payroll Benefits ($000's)	NPS Jobs	Total Jobs	Labor Income ($000's)	Value Added ($000's)
Cedar Breaks NM	608	125	16	20	845	946
Chaco Culture NHP	1,640	410	35	40	2,204	2,352
Chamizal NMEM	1,352	422	30	37	1,995	2,211
Channel Islands NP	4,536	1,218	87	107	6,705	7,474
Charles Pinckney NHS	370	107	6	9	555	628
Chattahoochee River NRA	2,247	621	42	52	3,298	3,663
Chesapeake & Ohio Canal NHP	7,200	1,948	147	172	10,431	11,507
Chickamauga & Chattanooga NMP	2,294	644	49	64	3,483	3,955
Chickasaw NRA	2,985	849	76	91	4,238	4,637
Chiricahua NM	913	243	21	23	1,227	1,308
Christiansted NHS	776	193	12	15	1,037	1,110
City of Rocks NRES	25	7	2	2	35	37
Clara Barton NHS	454	129	11	13	664	732
Colonial NHP	4,388	1,241	84	104	6,205	6,935
Colorado NM	1,838	452	38	46	2,548	2,788
Congaree Swamp NM	1,050	318	24	31	1,606	1,808
Coronado NMEM	1,084	357	19	24	1,615	1,773
Cowpens NB	457	121	13	16	682	770
Crater Lake NP	4,857	1,127	106	129	6,739	7,374
Craters of the Moon NM	1,178	324	21	24	1,582	1,673
Cumberland Gap NHP	2,703	840	57	68	3,863	4,190
Cumberland Island NS	1,616	505	27	37	2,489	2,801
Curecanti NRA	2,853	727	58	68	3,844	4,144
Cuyahoga Valley NP	8,284	2,125	178	220	12,112	13,499
Dayton Aviation Heritage NHP	1,183	297	23	30	1,740	1,952
De Soto NMEM	500	132	12	16	788	917
Death Valley NP	7,054	1,907	144	145	8,988	9,018
Delaware Water Gap NRA	7,344	1,882	121	164	10,919	12,404
Denali NP & Pres	12,495	2,552	209	212	15,156	15,227
Devils Tower NM	1,113	272	25	31	1,564	1,724
Dinosaur NM	2,468	640	53	60	3,347	3,623
Dry Tortugas NP	848	214	16	20	1,190	1,336
Edgar Allan Poe NHS	293	92	5	7	473	543
Effigy Mounds NM	1,053	226	31	36	1,423	1,559
Eisenhower NHS	852	249	16	19	1,201	1,305
El Malpais NM	1,301	397	28	38	2,024	2,303
El Morro NM	572	158	14	16	782	846
Eleanor Roosevelt NHS	265	53	7	8	366	409
Eugene O'Neill NHS	365	94	8	10	557	636
Everglades NP	17,425	5,032	304	408	26,701	30,211
Federal Hall NMEM	279	71	10	11	416	469

Park Unit	Park Payroll			Impacts of Park Payroll		
	Salary ($000's)	Payroll Benefits ($000's)	NPS Jobs	Total Jobs	Labor Income ($000's)	Value Added ($000's)
Fire Island NS	3,344	814	57	72	4,934	5,574
Flight 93 NMEM	573	130	11	15	808	896
Florissant Fossil Beds NM	752	202	19	22	1,072	1,186
Fort Bowie NHS	258	71	6	7	349	372
Fort Caroline NMEM	1,563	436	37	46	2,358	2,661
Fort Davis NHS	965	242	23	26	1,281	1,379
Fort Donelson NB	906	274	18	21	1,271	1,367
Fort Frederica NM	487	159	10	12	724	796
Fort Laramie NHS	1,172	316	27	32	1,643	1,800
Fort Larned NHS	707	214	17	21	1,028	1,120
Fort Matanzas NM	101	39	3	3	153	168
Fort McHenry NM & HS	1,669	410	40	46	2,333	2,561
Fort Necessity NB	1,008	306	18	24	1,472	1,620
Fort Point NHS	342	72	6	7	485	545
Fort Pulaski NM	1,020	219	28	34	1,446	1,629
Fort Raleigh NHS	265	72	10	12	389	441
Fort Scott NHS	871	194	18	21	1,162	1,267
Fort Smith NHS	678	189	15	19	976	1,071
Fort Stanwix NM	929	269	19	23	1,339	1,453
Fort Sumter NM	1,308	329	27	35	1,913	2,170
Fort Union NM	844	203	23	27	1,152	1,255
Fort Union Trading Post NHS	585	124	14	16	781	849
Fort Vancouver NHS	1,610	406	38	50	2,494	2,879
Fossil Butte NM	519	123	11	13	700	764
Frederick Douglass NHS	415	68	12	14	556	618
Frederick Law Olmsted NHS	1,232	335	19	24	1,887	2,125
Fredericksburg & Spotsylvania NMP	3,071	812	55	66	4,252	4,693
Friendship Hill NHS	450	161	7	10	682	748
Gates of the Arctic NP & Pres	1,585	366	37	45	2,283	2,585
Gateway NRA	18,772	4,277	361	433	27,521	31,071
Gauley River NRA	541	228	12	14	859	935
General Grant NMEM	220	67	6	6	339	381
George Rogers Clark NHP	616	178	12	15	856	922
George Washington Birthplace N	1,024	279	29	32	1,388	1,509
George Washington Carver NM	734	177	17	21	1,019	1,114
George Washington Memorial Pkwy	6,506	1,712	134	156	9,377	10,349
Gettysburg NMP	4,963	1,145	71	90	6,693	7,296
Gila Cliff Dwellings NM	236	53	5	5	304	324
Glacier Bay NP & Pres	4,902	1,181	72	98	7,113	8,047
Glacier NP	12,176	2,875	286	362	17,349	19,510
Glen Canyon NRA	8,441	2,280	182	209	11,615	12,528
Golden Gate NRA	14,669	3,779	265	337	22,267	25,391
Golden Spike NHS	656	190	15	18	947	1,037

Table A-2. (Continued)

Park Unit	Park Payroll			Impacts of Park Payroll		
	Salary ($000's)	Payroll Benefits ($000's)	NPS Jobs	Total Jobs	Labor Income ($000's)	Value Added ($000's)
Governors Island NM	738	153	14	17	1,066	1,205
Grand Canyon NP	26,870	7,448	571	658	37,236	40,174
Grand Portage NM	735	189	17	20	1,003	1,089
Grand Teton NP	12,741	3,318	284	335	17,644	19,375
Grant-Kohrs Ranch NHS	926	251	22	28	1,364	1,529
Great Basin NP	2,425	648	52	56	3,165	3,346
Great Sand Dunes NM	1,929	474	35	43	2,630	2,840
Great Smoky Mountains NP	14,993	4,426	339	399	21,284	23,320
Greenbelt Park	759	174	14	17	1,068	1,181
Guadalupe Mountains NP	2,112	588	60	65	2,853	3,033
Guilford Courthouse NMP	761	225	17	22	1,180	1,337
Gulf Islands NS	5,389	1,435	127	158	7,823	8,781
Hagerman Fossil Beds NM	498	116	11	14	682	749
Haleakala NP	4,695	1,225	95	121	6,860	7,744
Hamilton Grange NMEM	157	45	3	4	239	269
Hampton NHS	984	252	28	32	1,386	1,520
Harpers Ferry NHP	5,372	1,502	116	137	7,662	8,414
Harry S Truman NHS	898	270	19	31	1,690	2,088
Hawaii Volcanoes NP	7,290	1,873	148	194	10,707	12,144
Herbert Hoover NHS	1,005	264	24	30	1,469	1,649
Home of Franklin D. Roosevelt	901	265	18	22	1,329	1,477
Homestead National Monument of America	877	256	24	30	1,302	1,447
Hopewell Culture NHP	706	156	17	20	958	1,053
Hopewell Furnace NHS	1,149	267	19	26	1,675	1,897
Horseshoe Bend NMP	509	150	12	14	727	798
Hot Springs NP	3,245	824	73	90	4,539	4,991
Hovenweep NM	387	121	7	9	556	607
Hubbell Trading Post NHS	714	169	14	15	915	974
Independence NHP	12,293	3,320	179	255	19,337	22,269
Indiana Dunes NL	6,828	1,891	129	169	10,033	11,226
Isle Royale NP	3,190	763	64	78	4,338	4,726
Jean Lafitte NHP & PRES	3,069	904	58	75	4,633	5,198
Jefferson National Expansion Memorial	8,090	2,472	180	221	12,112	13,434
Jewel Cave NM	1,019	233	30	36	1,451	1,623
Jimmy Carter NHS	898	293	20	24	1,294	1,404
John D Rockefeller Jr. Mem Pkwy	413	117	7	9	581	634
John Day Fossil Beds NM	1,099	305	24	25	1,451	1,507
John Fitzgerald Kennedy NHS	373	90	7	9	561	633
John Muir NHS	765	189	15	19	1,124	1,271

Park Unit	Park Payroll			Impacts of Park Payroll		
	Salary ($000's)	Payroll Benefits ($000's)	NPS Jobs	Total Jobs	Labor Income ($000's)	Value Added ($000's)
Johnstown Flood NMEM	573	176	13	16	863	961
Joshua Tree NP	6,338	1,699	140	162	8,837	9,604
Kalaupapa NHP	2,430	658	40	53	3,575	4,032
Kaloko-Honokohau NHP	1,113	336	24	31	1,686	1,905
Katmai NP & Pres/Aniakchak	2,974	649	44	44	3,623	3,623
Kenai Fjords NP	2,214	493	40	51	3,172	3,594
Kennesaw Mountain NBP	1,051	302	21	27	1,630	1,865
Kings Mountain NMP	811	210	19	23	1,136	1,248
Klondike Gold Rush NHP Alaska	2,660	622	39	54	3,840	4,347
Klondike Gold Rush NHP Seattle	492	136	15	18	768	885
Knife River Indian Villages NHS	582	160	14	17	862	958
Lake Clark NP & Pres	1,922	500	32	42	2,826	3,192
Lake Mead NRA	16,833	4,605	354	402	23,296	25,057
Lake Meredith NRA	2,336	712	51	54	3,178	3,255
Lake Roosevelt NRA	3,521	961	74	91	5,005	5,493
Lassen Volcanic NP	4,384	1,074	84	109	6,340	7,079
Lava Beds NM	2,061	583	45	52	2,883	3,105
LBJ Memorial Grove on the Potomac	33	9	3	3	48	53
Lewis & Clark National Historic	1,105	290	29	32	1,491	1,595
Lincoln Boyhood NMEM	690	208	16	19	991	1,087
Lincoln Home NHS	1,911	492	43	52	2,714	2,970
Little Bighorn Battlefield NM	980	243	23	29	1,420	1,593
Little River Canyon NPRES	966	285	23	28	1,401	1,545
Little Rock Central High School	694	188	15	19	1,015	1,120
Longfellow NHS	771	178	12	15	1,108	1,243
Lowell NHP	5,349	1,348	98	122	7,803	8,736
Lyndon B. Johnson NHP	2,348	668	54	64	3,407	3,757
Maggie L Walker NHS	422	103	10	12	619	699
Mammoth Cave NP	6,055	1,431	172	200	8,304	9,027
Manassas NBP	1,935	533	29	36	2,757	3,046
Manzanar NHS	883	216	16	18	1,154	1,228
Marsh-Billings Rockefeller NHP	1,286	301	26	33	1,862	2,092
Martin Luther King Jr NHS	2,084	491	42	51	2,975	3,313
Martin Van Buren NHS	818	191	18	21	1,140	1,243
Mary McLeod Bethune Council House NHS	475	96	12	13	656	727
Mesa Verde NP	5,739	1,381	131	154	7,917	8,682
Minute Man NHP	2,042	495	34	43	2,959	3,315
Missouri National Recreational	492	133	13	15	673	726
Mojave NPRES	3,740	1,093	69	86	5,609	6,232
Monocacy NB	1,250	356	24	29	1,819	2,018
Montezuma Castle NM	1,534	435	35	46	2,404	2,769
Moores Creek NB	308	92	8	10	455	512
Morristown NHP	1,824	499	29	37	2,707	3,041

Table A-2. (Continued)

Park Unit	Park Payroll			Impacts of Park Payroll		
	Salary ($000's)	Payroll Benefits ($000's)	NPS Jobs	Total Jobs	Labor Income ($000's)	Value Added ($000's)
Mount Rainier NP	10,547	2,473	232	283	14,957	16,620
Mount Rushmore NMEM	3,418	1,008	69	90	5,102	5,682
Muir Woods NM	784	195	14	17	1,171	1,330
Natchez NHP	998	324	21	23	1,375	1,462
Natchez Trace Parkway	7,176	2,424	156	178	10,228	10,902
National Capital Parks Central	14,278	3,593	288	338	20,416	22,549
National Capital Parks East	8,304	2,129	148	177	11,914	13,155
Natural Bridges NM	417	95	9	10	534	570
Navajo NM	745	175	18	21	1,000	1,083
New Bedford Whaling NHP	462	111	10	13	677	769
New Orleans Jazz NHP	551	157	15	18	827	928
New River Gorge NR	5,362	1,638	111	111	7,000	7,000
Nez Perce NHP	1,901	530	39	48	2,719	2,978
Nicodemus NHS	336	97	8	8	433	433
Ninety Six NHS	308	92	8	9	438	479
Niobrara NSR	540	153	12	14	747	804
North Cascades NP	7,152	1,905	152	192	10,909	12,504
Obed Wild and Scenic River	493	161	10	12	718	779
Ocmulgee NM	813	178	18	23	1,145	1,279
Olympic NP	10,885	2,835	229	278	15,238	16,777
Oregon Caves NM	1,154	268	28	35	1,633	1,811
Organ Pipe Cactus NM	2,488	758	40	58	3,971	4,575
Ozark National Scenic Riverways	5,242	1,517	91	127	7,831	8,752
Padre Island NS	3,470	903	75	96	5,083	5,660
Palo Alto Battlefield NHS	599	153	15	18	862	955
Pea Ridge NMP	881	240	23	27	1,233	1,350
Pecos NHP	1,340	425	29	39	2,092	2,367
Perry's Victory and Internatl Peace Mem	801	218	17	22	1,182	1,315
Petersburg NB	2,225	623	39	52	3,283	3,715
Petrified Forest NP	2,576	679	55	63	3,515	3,802
Petroglyph NM	1,231	312	25	35	1,865	2,138
Pictured Rocks NL	1,786	402	32	33	2,203	2,249
Pinnacles NM	2,444	646	48	56	3,486	3,858
Pipe Spring NM	808	201	18	22	1,133	1,247
Pipestone NM	506	141	12	16	765	866
Piscataway Park	294	77	7	8	424	468
Point Reyes NS	6,803	1,898	122	153	10,368	11,735
Prince William Forest Park	1,980	540	42	49	2,873	3,169
Pu'uhonua o Honaunau NHP	1,729	365	41	52	2,460	2,801
Puukohola Heiau NHS	1,005	235	25	31	1,453	1,651
Rainbow Bridge NM	95	27	3	3	132	142

Park Unit	Park Payroll			Impacts of Park Payroll		
	Salary ($000's)	Payroll Benefits ($000's)	NPS Jobs	Total Jobs	Labor Income ($000's)	Value Added ($000's)
Redwood NP	6,976	1,986	135	165	9,881	10,717
Richmond NBP	2,021	575	42	53	3,048	3,431
Rio Grande Wild and Scenic River	116	54	2	2	181	193
Rock Creek Park	3,775	923	79	92	5,371	5,936
Rocky Mountain NP	14,547	3,694	319	392	20,940	23,438
Roger Williams NMEM	370	103	9	12	589	678
Russell Cave NM	255	54	7	8	341	374
Sagamore Hill NHS	1,098	262	25	30	1,615	1,826
Saguaro NP	3,675	1,027	97	112	5,230	5,708
Saint Croix NSR	2,832	746	59	75	4,194	4,713
Saint Paul's Church NHS	5	2	1	1	8	9
Saint-Gaudens NHS	784	223	14	18	1,140	1,269
Salem Maritime NHS	1,902	474	44	51	2,694	2,981
Salinas Pueblo Missions NM	1,184	281	30	40	1,776	2,039
San Antonio Missions NHP	2,400	749	55	70	3,708	4,186
San Francisco Maritime NHP	5,828	1,570	83	103	8,602	9,627
San Juan Island NHP	696	186	14	17	966	1,047
San Juan NHS	3,386	834	87	107	4,877	5,483
Santa Monica Mountains NRA	6,027	1,726	123	149	9,017	10,039
Saratoga NHP	1,433	419	32	37	2,023	2,185
Saugus Iron Works NHS	660	174	15	18	1,000	1,124
Scotts Bluff NM	733	195	17	21	1,038	1,131
Sequoia NP/ Kings Canyon NP	17,027	4,274	358	431	23,986	26,354
Shenandoah NP	10,317	2,955	234	314	16,206	18,700
Shiloh NMP	1,655	431	39	47	2,310	2,546
Sitka NHP	1,173	310	20	26	1,729	1,952
Sleeping Bear Dunes NL	3,915	808	85	111	5,615	6,411
Springfield Armory NHS	864	173	18	23	1,271	1,457
Statue of Liberty NM	9,582	2,391	200	237	14,255	16,067
Steamtown NHS	3,499	988	48	71	5,327	5,986
Stones River NB	994	223	24	30	1,510	1,734
Tallgrass Prairie NPRES	610	147	13	15	800	848
Thaddeus Kosciuszko NMEM	115	38	3	4	188	215
Theodore Roosevelt Birthplace NHS	168	52	4	5	259	291
Theodore Roosevelt Island	75	23	2	2	112	123
Theodore Roosevelt NP	2,254	628	56	68	3,224	3,518
Thomas Edison NHP	1,915	446	31	39	2,780	3,133
Thomas Stone NHS	446	105	18	20	610	673
Timpanogos Cave NM	1,268	244	43	53	1,830	2,087
Tonto NM	723	219	15	20	1,159	1,342
Tumacacori NHP	962	273	18	22	1,390	1,530
Tuskegee Airmen NHS	304	87	7	8	425	463
Tuskegee Institute NHS	634	161	13	16	865	944

Table A-2. (Continued)

Park Unit	Park Payroll			Impacts of Park Payroll		
	Salary ($000's)	Payroll Benefits ($000's)	NPS Jobs	Total Jobs	Labor Income ($000's)	Value Added ($000's)
Ulysses S. Grant NHS	752	193	20	24	1,089	1,212
Upper Delaware SRR	1,943	517	33	40	2,696	2,956
Valley Forge NHP	4,672	1,248	67	95	7,326	8,433
Vanderbilt Mansion NHS	624	182	15	18	918	1,021
Vicksburg NMP	1,958	559	45	55	2,846	3,120
Virgin Islands NP	3,126	878	64	82	4,611	5,170
Voyageurs NP	3,473	932	65	84	4,999	5,486
Walnut Canyon NM	33	9	2	2	46	50
Washita Battlefield NHS	421	142	13	14	608	655
Weir Farm NHS	822	214	14	17	1,188	1,324
Whiskeytown-Shasta-Trinity NRA	3,952	1,100	89	109	5,765	6,357
White House	6,272	1,562	122	144	8,951	9,888
White Sands NM	1,158	324	30	34	1,582	1,697
Whitman Mission NHS	608	149	12	15	851	932
William Howard Taft NHS	495	138	10	12	746	834
Wilson's Creek NB	1,725	466	37	49	2,594	2,917
Wind Cave NP	3,334	868	85	101	4,815	5,341
Wolf Trap Farm Park	2,927	671	74	84	4,119	4,556
Women's Rights NHP	904	256	16	20	1,289	1,411
World War II Valor in the Pacific NM	2,007	507	43	58	3,078	3,543
Wrangell-St Elias NP & Pres	3,964	814	63	84	5,610	6,366
Wright Brothers NMEM	207	46	6	7	294	334
Wupatki NM	2,378	648	50	59	3,326	3,609
Yellowstone NP	29,899	8,116	566	691	41,899	46,072
Yosemite NP	39,283	10,123	892	1005	53,199	57,156
Yukon-Charley Rivers NPRES	1,356	306	36	43	1,947	2,206
Zion NP	8,694	2,415	210	265	12,672	14,060

Notes: Jobs include part-time and full-time jobs with seasonal positions adjusted to an annual basis. NPS jobs, salary, and benefits are assigned to the unit where the employee's time was charged, which may differ from their duty station. Economic impacts include NPS payroll and jobs plus the induced effects of NPS employee spending of their wages and salaries in the local region. Jobs are rounded to the nearest job.

Table A-3. Payroll Impacts of National Park Units on Local Economies, Administrative Units and Parks without Visit Counts, FY 2010

Park Unit	Park Payroll			Impacts of Park Payroll		
	Salary ($000's)	Payroll Benefits ($000's)	NPS Jobs	Total Jobs	Labor Income ($000's)	Value Added ($000's)
Administration Team Coord, PGSO	10,136	2,457	158	211	15,012	17,028
African Burial Grounds	703	136	18	22	981	1,104
Ala Kahakai NHT	226	65	3	4	320	348
Alaska Regional Office	5,014	1,125	70	97	7,148	8,030
Alaska Support Office	9,897	2,283	160	191	13,045	13,976
American Memorial Park	865	237	17	20	1,212	1,318
Anacostia Park	1	0	1	1	2	2
Anchorage Interagency Visitors Center	477	81	11	14	654	738
Appalachian NST	893	250	15	20	1,324	1,481
Associate Reg Dir, Administration	10,100	2,516	147	202	14,649	16,426
Biological Resources Mgmt Division	2,103	540	25	36	3,066	3,436
Blackstone River Valley NHC	732	200	12	16	1,079	1,208
Boston Harbor Islands NRA	853	186	20	25	1,211	1,361
Boston Support Office	889	224	10	14	1,292	1,448
Cedar Creek and Belle Grove NHP	309	69	4	6	452	513
Center For Urban Ecology	214	42	6	7	298	336
Chesapeake Bay Program Office	1,195	320	16	23	1,756	1,966
Chihuahuan Desert Network	312	92	5	7	466	521
Columbia Cascades So	6,229	1,604	85	117	9,319	10,558
Denver Service Center	19,679	4,962	508	617	28,602	32,065
Ebey's Landing NHRES	304	82	5	7	424	462
Erie Canalway NHC	220	69	4	5	317	344
Fairbanks Interagency Visitors Center	429	90	12	14	574	626
Flagstaff Areas	90	18	5	5	127	142
FLETC (Fed Law Enforcement Tng Ctr)	1,918	634	67	78	2,939	3,276
Glen Echo Park	198	55	6	7	278	302
Gloria Dei Church NHS	23	7	2	2	33	36
Great Falls Park	815	210	20	25	1,189	1,332
Great Lakes Network	761	230	16	20	1,144	1,278
Greater Yellowstone Network	432	107	8	10	627	703
Harbor Parks	618	167	10	13	909	1,018
Harpers Ferry Center	9,394	2,297	176	215	12,887	14,042
Heartland Network	516	169	10	13	789	880
Historic Preservation Training Ctr (HPTC)	262	73	9	10	387	433
Horace Albright Training Ctr	0	0	1	1	0	0
Ice Age NST	312	83	6	8	436	474

Table A-3. (Continued)

	Park Payroll			Impacts of Park Payroll		
Park Unit	Salary ($000's)	Payroll Benefits ($000's)	NPS Jobs	Total Jobs	Labor Income ($000's)	Value Added ($000's)
Intermountain Nr-Pro	948	255	18	23	1,394	1,561
Intermountain Regional Office	26,093	6,689	400	544	38,033	42,624
Keweenaw NHP	1,259	289	30	34	1,658	1,776
Land Acquisition Project Office	474	123	7	9	710	805
Lewis & Clark NHT	1,127	347	18	23	1,618	1,757
Manhattan Sites	1,118	273	20	26	1,616	1,813
Mather Training Ctr	0	0	0	0	0	0
Midwest Archeological Center	1,670	406	35	43	2,475	2,807
Midwest Regional Office	16,526	4,248	253	344	24,099	27,007
Minidoka Internment NM	194	52	6	7	271	294
Mississippi NR&RA	1,584	414	31	39	2,376	2,691
Museum Resources Ctr	441	102	7	10	632	710
National Capital Regional Office	3,671	838	62	83	5,247	5,893
National Information Systems CNTR	205	44	4	5	290	326
National Information Technology CNTR	186	10	16	17	233	266
National Interagency Fire Center	4,722	1,485	72	97	7,335	8,274
National Mall	4,991	1,093	142	169	7,088	7,966
National Parks Of New York Harbor	559	125	6	10	797	895
National Trails System, Santa Fe	1,360	392	19	26	2,076	2,347
Natl Ctr For Rec & Conservation	1,478	400	19	27	2,176	2,436
NER Historic Architecture Program	485	102	7	9	703	799
North Country NST	275	74	6	7	414	469
Northeast Education Services Center	13	2	1	1	19	21
Northeast Museum Services Center	703	189	9	13	1,060	1,200
Northeast Regional Office	24,922	6,270	342	473	37,140	42,095
Northern Colorado Plateau Network	744	217	18	22	1,112	1,243
Northern Great Plains Network	368	110	9	11	552	617
NP Of American Samoa	1,144	226	27	31	1,515	1,656
Office Of The Chief Information Officer	8,579	2,109	78	126	12,415	13,925
Office Of The Director	92,546	22,471	1,311	1,822	133,643	149,925
Office Of Wyoming State Coordinator	110	32	1	2	169	191
Old Post Office Tower	411	110	8	11	603	676
Olmstead Center For Landscape Preservation	685	193	14	18	1,041	1,178
Overmountain Victory NHT	88	18	2	2	126	144
Pacific Island Support Office	737	167	10	13	1,080	1,226

Park Unit	Park Payroll			Impacts of Park Payroll		
	Salary ($000's)	Payroll Benefits ($000's)	NPS Jobs	Total Jobs	Labor Income ($000's)	Value Added ($000's)
Pacific West Regional Office	8,975	2,143	158	205	13,260	15,044
Parashant NM	710	198	15	18	1,078	1,219
Pinelands NRES (Interp Pgm)	155	44	3	3	236	266
Potomac Heritage NST	125	38	3	3	188	210
Presidio Of San Francisco	8,279	2,508	138	184	12,452	13,909
Rocky Mountain Network	456	116	8	11	664	744
Roosevelt-Vanderbilt Headquarters	2,129	472	42	54	3,029	3,404
Rosie the Riveter WW II Home Front NHP	739	188	12	16	1,075	1,205
Saint Croix Island International HS	182	32	5	6	258	294
Salt River Bay NHP & Ecological PRES	234	68	5	6	358	405
Sand Creek Massacre NHS	394	117	10	13	605	683
SE Archeological Center	1,385	371	32	40	2,086	2,361
Selma To Montgomery NHT	118	35	5	5	181	204
Sonoran Desert Network	596	164	14	18	880	984
Southeast Regional Office	24,996	6,162	369	500	37,123	42,094
Southern Arizona Group	708	201	13	16	1,078	1,219
Southern Colorado Plateau Network	716	226	12	16	1,086	1,212
Southern Plains Network	269	61	5	7	384	432
Spanish Colonial Research Center	99	32	2	3	155	174
Strategic Planning Division	180	50	2	3	266	297
United States Park Police	69,452	24,944	1,058	1,442	108,373	120,592
Virgin Islands Coral Reef NM	210	74	8	9	334	375
Washington Training Ctr	9	2	1	1	13	15
Western Archeological & Conservation Center	700	171	12	16	1,038	1,177
Western Arctic National Parklands	1,917	446	32	42	2,821	3,202
Yucca House NM	61	23	2	2	99	111

Notes: Jobs include part-time and full-time jobs with seasonal positions adjusted to an annual basis. NPS jobs, salary, and benefits are assigned to the unit where the employee's time was charged, which may differ from their duty station. Economic impacts include NPS payroll and jobs plus the induced effects of NPS employee spending of their wages and salaries in the local region. Jobs are rounded to the nearest job.

Table A-4. Impacts of NPS Visitor Spending and Payroll on Local Economies by State, 2010

State	Recreation Visits	Non-Local Visitor Spending ($000's)	Jobs from Non-Local Visitor Spending	Payroll-related Jobs	Total Jobs
Alabama	781,550	19,043	311	92	403
Alaska	2,274,781	208,185	2,637	1,061	3,698
American Samoa	0	0		52	52
Arizona	10,546,150	671,467	9,661	1,351	11,012
Arkansas	3,125,664	137,996	2,216	302	2,518
California	34,633,664	1,076,998	13,822	4,022	17,844
Colorado	5,631,244	292,721	4,345	2,021	6,366
Connecticut	19,313	1,162	13	17	30
District of Columbia	33,140,005	908,844	10,875	5,481	16,356
Florida	9,222,981	513,999	7,608	922	8,530
Georgia	6,776,556	214,277	3,036	865	3,901
Guam	219,349	7,109	85	0	85
Hawaii	4,493,123	235,974	3,195	545	3,740
Idaho	530,977	19,661	298	192	490
Illinois	354,125	18,178	285	52	336
Indiana	2,395,485	55,805	847	203	1,050
Iowa	222,295	11,028	192	67	258
Kansas	100,361	4,429	76	83	159
Kentucky	1,797,894	86,016	1,409	311	1,721
Louisiana	496,329	22,978	332	111	443
Maine	2,504,208	183,491	3,147	190	3,337
Maryland	3,541,570	164,885	2,198	386	2,583
Massachusetts	9,913,501	393,235	5,297	671	5,968
Michigan	1,796,006	139,901	2,438	256	2,694
Minnesota	540,195	29,690	486	196	682
Mississippi	6,588,026	79,329	1,171	260	1,431
Missouri	4,140,544	155,992	2,427	474	2,900
Montana	4,584,011	291,405	4,390	804	5,194
Nebraska	290,323	9,538	179	145	323
Nevada	5,399,439	166,479	1,894	376	2,269
New Hampshire	30,941	1,076	17	18	35
New Jersey	5,858,443	121,506	1,848	278	2,127
New Mexico	1,657,550	65,411	976	545	1,521
New York	17,389,242	362,301	4,256	1,039	5,295
North Carolina	17,093,464	701,499	10,404	669	11,073
North Dakota	659,927	29,753	531	102	633
Ohio	2,738,275	53,289	858	304	1,163
Oklahoma	1,266,189	13,735	182	105	287
Oregon	888,358	53,059	831	222	1,053
Pennsylvania	8,970,475	314,246	4,858	1,270	6,127

State	Recreation Visits	Non-Local Visitor Spending ($000's)	Jobs from Non-Local Visitor Spending	Payroll-related Jobs	Total Jobs
Puerto Rico	1,105,252	51,169	781	107	888
Rhode Island	51,559	3,103	49	12	61
South Carolina	1,529,172	42,799	679	125	804
South Dakota	4,199,267	162,442	2,758	346	3,104
Tennessee	7,898,557	519,702	7,538	445	7,983
Texas	5,495,156	215,964	3,312	674	3,986
Utah	8,975,525	611,714	9,267	904	10,171
Vermont	31,209	1,445	21	33	54
Virgin Islands	638,094	66,680	1,169	116	1,285
Virginia	22,708,338	505,962	7,294	1,264	8,558
Washington	7,281,785	242,467	3,611	950	4,560
West Virginia	1,811,722	59,713	785	488	1,273
Wisconsin	251,145	19,415	327	100	427
Wyoming	6,307,997	610,634	9,059	786	9,845
Total	280,897,309	10,948,899	156,279	32,407	188,686

Notes: Payroll-related jobs include NPS jobs and the induced effects of the NPS payroll on the local economy, covering parks with visit counts (Table A-2) as well as administrative units and parks without visit counts (Table A-3). Total job impacts include those supported by non-local visitor spending and the NPS payroll. For 20 parks with property in more than one state, activity is allocated using the proportions in Table A-6.

Table A-5. Impacts of NPS Visitor Spending and Payroll on Local Economies by Region, 2010

Region	Recreation Visits	Non-Local Spending ($ Millions)	Jobs from Non-Local Visitor Spending	Payroll-related Jobs	Total Jobs
Alaska	2,274,781	208	2,637	1,061	3,698
Harpers Ferry		0		215	215
Intermountain	42,648,861	2,717	40,554	7,090	47,644
Midwest	20,804,846	827	13,610	2,627	16,237
National Capital	45,271,135	1,119	13,445	2,064	15,509
Northeast	55,118,574	1,795	25,642	4,569	30,211
Pacific West	55,261,655	1,857	24,373	6,458	30,831
Southeast	59,517,457	2,425	36,018	4,143	40,161
Washington Office				4,179	4,179
Total	280,897,309	10,949	156,279	32,407	188,686

Notes: Payroll-related jobs include NPS jobs and the induced effects of the NPS payroll on the local economy, covering parks with visit counts (Table A-2) as well as administrative units and parks without visit counts (Table A-3). Total job impacts include those supported by non-local visitor spending and the NPS payroll.

Table A-6. Allocations to States for Multi-state Parks

Park	State	Share
Assateague Island NS	MD	33%
Assateague Island NS	VA	67%
Bighorn Canyon NRA	WY	46%
Bighorn Canyon NRA	MT	54%
Big South Fork NRRA	KY	41%
Big South Fork NRRA	TN	59%
Blue Ridge Parkway	VA	38%
Blue Ridge Parkway	NC	62%
Chickamauga & Chattanooga NMP	GA	50%
Chickamauga & Chattanooga NMP	TN	50%
Chesapeake & Ohio Canal NHP	WV	6%
Chesapeake & Ohio Canal NHP	MD	9%
Chesapeake & Ohio Canal NHP	DC	85%
Cumberland Gap NHP	KY	93%
Cumberland Gap NHP	VA	7%
Delaware Water Gap NRA	PA	29%
Delaware Water Gap NRA	NJ	71%
Dinosaur NM	UT	26%
Dinosaur NM	CO	74%
Gateway NRA	NJ	20%
Gateway NRA	NY	80%
Glen Canyon NRA	AZ	8%
Glen Canyon NRA	UT	92%
Great Smoky Mountains NP	NC	44%
Great Smoky Mountains NP	TN	56%
Gulf Islands Nat Seashore	MS	25%
Gulf Islands Nat Seashore	FL	75%
Hovenweep NM	CO	44%
Hovenweep NM	UT	56%
Lake Mead NRA	AZ	25%
Lake Mead NRA	NV	75%
Natchez Trace Parkway	AL	7%
Natchez Trace Parkway	TN	13%
Natchez Trace Parkway	MS	80%
National capital Parks East	MD	10%
National capital Parks East	DC	90%
Saint Croix Nat scenic river	MN	50%
Saint Croix Nat scenic river	WI	50%
Upper Delaware SRR	NY	50%
Upper Delaware SRR	PA	50%
Yellowstone NP	WY	49%
Yellowstone NP	MT	51%

End Notes

[1] National estimates use multipliers for the U.S. economy.

[2] Jobs include full-time and part-time jobs. Seasonal positions are adjusted to an annual basis. Labor income covers wages and salaries, including income of sole proprietors and payroll benefits. Value added is the sum of labor income, profits and rents, and indirect business taxes. It can also be defined as total sales net of the costs of all non-labor inputs. Value added is the preferred economic measure of the contribution of an industry or activity to the economy.

[3] The 60-mile radius is a general average representing the primary impact region around most parks. The radius is closer to 30 miles for parks in urban settings and as large as 100 miles for some western parks. Economic multipliers are based on regions defined as groupings of counties to approximate a 60-mile radius of the park.

[4] These studies are conducted by the Visitor Services Project (VSP) at the University of Idaho. Reports for individual parks are available at their website: http://www.psu.uidaho.edu /vsp.reports.htm

[5] For example, spending during extended stays in an area visiting relatives, on business, or when the park visit was not the primary trip purpose is excluded. For most historic sites and parks in urban areas, spending for one day or night is counted for each park entry. Where several park units are within a 60-mile radius, adjustments are made for those visiting more than one park on the same day.

[6] Day trips include pass-thru visitors not spending a night within 60 miles of the park as well as stays with friends and relatives and in owned seasonal homes.

[7] Spending figures exclude airfares and other trip spending beyond 60 miles of the park. Purchases of durable goods (boats, RVs) and major equipment are also excluded. Special expenses for commercial rafting trips, air overflights and other special activities are not fully captured for all parks.

[8] To the extent possible, spending not directly associated with a park visit is also excluded. For example, only one night's expenses are counted for visitors in the area primarily on business, visiting relatives, or visiting other attractions. For parks with visitor surveys, spending attributed to a park visit was estimated based on the percentage of visitors identifying the park visit as the primary purpose of the trip.

[9] Secondary effects include indirect effects of businesses buying goods and services from backward-linked local firms and induced effects of household spending of their earnings.

[10] Local economic ratios are therefore used to estimate the direct effects. National multipliers are used to estimate secondary effects. With the exception of wholesale trade and manufacturing sectors, the national direct effects (Table 5) are therefore the same as the local direct effects (Table 4).

[11] The number of employees is estimated as an annual average for each park, so that seasonal positions are converted to annual equivalents. However, the job estimates include both full-time and part-time positions.

[12] There will be some double counting of camping fees as payments to concessionaires could not be fully sorted out from payments to the National Park Service.

[13] Visits are classified as local day trips, non-local day trips, and overnight trips staying in campgrounds or hotels, lodges, cabins, and bed and breakfasts. For parks with lodging facilities within the park, visitors staying in park lodges, campgrounds, or backcountry sites are distinguished from those staying outside the park in motels or nonNPS campgrounds.

Visitors staying with friends or relatives, in owned seasonal homes, or passing through without a local overnight stay are generally treated as day trips.

[14] Detailed impact reports for parks that have included economic questions in their VSP studies are available at the MGM2 (http://web4.canr.msu.edu/mgm2/) or NPS social science websites (http://www.nature.nps.gov/socialscience/products.cfm#MGM2Reports).

[15] Multipliers were adjusted by a factor of 1.1359 to account for the share of federal payroll that IMPLAN assigns to capital depreciation.

INDEX

A

B

C

D

E

F

G

H

I

J

K

L

M

T

U

V

W